14.00
9958B

MEDICINE AND THE OTHER DISCIPLINES

NUMBERS XIX/XX OF
THE NEW YORK ACADEMY OF MEDICINE
LECTURES TO THE LAITY

MEDICINE AND THE OTHER DISCIPLINES

LECTURES TO THE LAITY, NOS. XIX/XX

THE NEW YORK ACADEMY OF MEDICINE

Iago Galdston, M.D., Editor

INTERNATIONAL UNIVERSITIES PRESS, INC.

NEW YORK 1960

Copyright, 1959

International Universities Press, Inc., New York

Library of Congress Catalog Card Number: 59-15725

Printed in the United States of America

CONTENTS

FOREWORD

THE Committee on Lectures to the Laity of The New York Academy of Medicine has, from its inception, commanded distinguished doctors and scientists as speakers on the programs. A cursory survey of the list of speakers during the last twenty years shows an amazing list of doctors and scientists, who proved to be outstanding in the specialty on which they lectured.

A modern education in medicine and science could be obtained if one were able to read and retain even part of the subject matter covered through these years. The same holds true for the nineteenth and twentieth series of lectures published in this current volume.

Norbert Wiener, Ph.D., of the Massachusetts Institute of Technology, has on more than one occasion given a stimulating lecture on some phase of physics in medicine. He repeated it in this series. He showed the historical and contemporaneous application of physics to medicine.

Theodore Shedlovsky, Ph.D., of the Rockefeller Institute for Medical Research, discussed the latest findings in the relation of electrochemistry to medicine. Electrochemistry has provided powerful tools for medical research.

Our own Clarence P. Oberndorf, M.D., of Columbia University, discussed the development of the practice of psychiatry through the years.

Professor Benjamin D. Paul, Ph.D., lectured on anthro-

7

pology and medicine. Derived from anthropos—man and logos—discourse, the relationship becomes evident.

Justice David W. Peck, LL.D., D.J.S., a friend of the Academy, gave an instructive and interesting lecture dealing with the impact of medicine upon the law, and the need for cooperation between the two professions. This is especially pertinent now, when the impact between patient and doctor sometimes leads to misunderstanding.

In the twentieth series of lectures we were favored with an equally brilliant and satisfying series of talks.

Sidney Farber, M.D., Professor of Pathology at Harvard Medical School, discussed the newest treatment of cancer by chemotherapy. This is a subject of increasing importance to doctors, and more so to patients. In some cases the results have been most encouraging. Chemotherapy has allowed the time of survival to be lengthened.

Psychiatry is a subject which attracts all of us. Jules H. Masserman, M.D., from Northwestern University, dealt with the treatment of psychiatric patients ranging from psychoanalysis to group therapy, and from electric shock to brain surgery.

The Philosopher Looks at Science was the topic chosen by Ernest Nagel, Ph.D., from Columbia University, who urged us to have faith in scientific reasoning.

D. Ewen Cameron, M.D., from McGill University, discussed Life is for Living. One should have an abiding faith in abilities to meet the problems of daily life, and pursue a course based on fundamental beliefs in religion, health and sound training.

We had, in this series of lectures, proof that The New York Academy of Medicine attracts speakers from our own country, from Canada, and now from England.

Aldwyn B. Stokes, M.D., from Oxford University and

London University, came to speak on Psychosomatic Notions. He reviewed the problems of man in health and
sickness.

Our last speaker of the series was Charles G. King,
Ph.D., D.Sc., who discussed peoples with insufficient food
and those with an overabundance of food, and the philosophy of living to the best advantage in each situation.

HAROLD B. KEYES, M.D.

INTRODUCTION

JUST as the ancients included under the term philosophy all pursuits of knowledge that were not strictly
utilitarian, so we moderns are prone to label as science
any system of organized information, including the utilitarian. The practice is commonplace but somewhat regrettable. Technology is not science, though precious in
its own competences. Nor can the arts be reduced to
science, even if some of their dimensions can be measured,
analyzed, and classified.

All the aforegoing is prelude to the affirmation that
medicine, so large a component of modern science, is older
than science, and retains much that is not alien to, but is
different from science and more akin with the arts. The
burden of this affirmation is elaborated in the series of
essays published herein. These essays show by how much
medicine is affected and influenced by "the changing pano-
rama of science," and also, "the reciprocal relations between medicine and the other disciplines."

An Introduction is hardly the fitting place to argue a
major issue, yet it may not be the wrong place to mention
it. There are some who believe that technologic science
will in time "take over medicine"; that diagnoses and
therapeutic indications will be worked out by electronic
computers fed elementary, objective data; that the physician (if any remain to deserve that title) will be an ancil-

lary functionary not unlike the attendant in an industrial automatized plant. There are others, however, who are persuaded that this cannot and will not ever eventuate; that medicine which antedated modern science by more than two thousand years will continue, as it has done in the past, to profit by all that both science and technology can proffer, and yet remain that discipline which Hippocrates celebrated as the art that derives its strength from the love of Man—"Where there is Love of Man there is also Love of the Art."

Lest the reader be led to believe that the contributors to this volume pointedly address themselves to this "major issue," the Editor hastens to say that such is not the case. They each deal with their respective subjects as, to name but two, Norbert Wiener with "The Application of Physics to Medicine," and Justice David W. Peck with "Where Law and Medicine Meet."

The over-all persuasion yielded by the broad excursions of the contributors adds up in the mind of the Editor to the convictions expressed.

To the distinguished contributors to this volume, The New York Academy of Medicine extends its deep gratitude and appreciation for their splendid services.

IAGO GALDSTON, M.D.

THE PHILOSOPHER LOOKS AT SCIENCE

By Ernest Nagel, Ph.D.

THERE IS an ancient and still influential tradition, according to which philosophy is the supreme architectonic science, competent to prescribe to all inferior disciplines the limits of their possible scope and the ultimate significance of their discoveries. It is not in the spirit of this tradition that the following reflections are offered. Philosophy, as I conceive it, has no special avenue to truth. Whatever knowledge it claims to have of the world, must be based, if the claim is warranted, either on the findings of the special sciences, or on the same sort of evidence which the special sciences themselves acknowledge. Philosophy is not a rival of science. It neither supplies a more adequate account of things than the sciences provide, nor does it lay bare the alleged "presuppositions" upon which the special sciences supposedly rest, but which they are incompetent to justify with the help of their own methods.

Philosophy is in part a commentary on science. Its task in this regard is two-fold. It aims to analyze the complex logical procedures by which the apparently remote and frequently strange objects of theoretical science are brought into relation with the concrete occurrences of

13

common experience, to specify the functions in inquiry which the abstract notions of scientific thought perform, and to make evident the conditions which must be instituted if warranted claims to knowledge are to be achieved. Secondly, it seeks to make explicit the import, for traditional schemas of morals and for habitual patterns of conduct, of fresh scientific discoveries and of the logical method with which the sciences operate. It is in this way that philosophy becomes a clarified expression of the broad significance of science for human life.

It is my special aim to present, not an exhaustive survey of current philosophies of science, but a brief characterization of what seem to me the dominant features of the intellectual method basic to modern science. It is my hope to indicate in this way the humane values implicit in the use and extension of that method, and to place in proper perspective current trends which seek in one way or another to limit the authority and scope of scientific reason.

What does a philosopher see when he looks at science? There are at least three distinguishable facets which science exhibits to him. The most obvious one, and the one by far the best advertised, is the practical control over nature which science yields. It would be tedious to rehearse the great contributions of modern science to human welfare, or even to mention the major branches of technology which have profited from advances in fundamental theoretical and experimental research. It is sufficient to note that applied science has transformed the face of the earth, and has brought into being our contemporary Western civilization. Although Francis Bacon lived before modern science achieved its most spectacular victories, he was in this regard a true prophet of things to come. His conception of the nature of scientific method is now generally recognized to be woefully inadequate. But he sensed correctly the power over things that was latent in the "new science" of the seventeenth century; and he expressed a fundamental aspiration of his own and of later generations when he declared that "the true and lawful goal of the sciences is none other than this: that human life be endowed with new discoveries and powers." Since the technological fruits of systematic inquiry can be appreciated even by those with no scientific training, it is this aspect of science which is most prominent in the popular literature and teaching of science. Indeed, the practically useful fruits of fundamental research have in recent years been frequently stressed, even by the researchers themselves, in an attempt to justify the cost to those who ultimately shoulder it by heavy governmental subsidy of apparently otiose scientific inquiry.

I do not share the outlook of those who minimize the value of the material goods which science as an improved and expanding technology contributes toward the enhancement of human life, and who attribute the so-called "materialism" of our age to the growth of scientific technology. I think, nevertheless, that science viewed as a set of practical controls over nature has been overemphasized in recent years, to the neglect of other of its aspects. It is certainly not the case that the achievement of immediately useful ends is the sole, or even the central, motive which actuates scientific inquiry. A false picture is created of the history of science and of the complex goals of systematic inquiry when that motive is made focal. Moreover, this emphasis tends to portray science as a miscellany of surprising wonders and gadgets, and to create an image of the scientist as a miracle-worker with a nostrum for every physical and

psychic ill, whose opinions, like those of successful business-
men and military leaders, are to be taken as authoritative
even on matters about which they have demonstrable in-
competence.

Nor can we afford to be complaisant about the widespread though mistaken tendency to make fundamental
research responsible for the social consequences of applied
science—an imputation of responsibility which appears
plausible when science and technology are identified, and
which is often used to justify attempts at restricting the
freedom to inquire when those consequences are admit-
tedly undesirable.

In any event, science is more than a set of practically
useful technologies. Science has another facet, consisting
of a body of conclusions, stated in propositional form and
often general in content, which are asserted as the warranted findings of special inquiries. According to an ancient formula, the aim of theoretical science is to "save the
phenomena," that is, to exhibit the events and processes
occurring in the world as instances of general principles
which formulate invariable patterns of relations between
things. Science as a body of universal laws or theories does
"save the phenomena" in this sense, and makes the world
intelligible. In achieving this objective, science satisfies
the craving to know and to understand, perhaps the most
powerful impulse leading men to engage in systematic
inquiry. In achieving this objective, science is a primary
force in the history of man for undermining superstitious
beliefs and practices, and for dissolving fears which thrive
on ignorance. Science as theoretical understanding is the
creator of the intellectual basis for a humane and liberal
civilization: it supplies the indispensable ground for eval-

uating inherited customs and for assessing traditional principles by which men habitually order their daily lives.

It was once taken for granted that no proposition is
genuinely scientific unless it is demonstrable from first
principles. It was assumed, moreover, that the hallmark of
scientific truth is truth capable of being known with complete certainty and capable of being apprehended as absolutely necessary. This conception of the nature of science
took geometry as its model. A little reflection shows, however, that not everything can be demonstrated, and that
some premises must be accepted without demonstration.
Accordingly, so classical rationalism maintained, if the
ideals of certainty and necessity are to be realized by a
science, the basic premises or first principles of the science
must be grasped in an immediate originative act of the
intellect as necessarily and self-evidently true.

The conception of scientific knowledge just outlined was
once plausible. Subsequent developments have shown,
however, that the body of scientific conclusions is not fixed
once and for all—not merely because additions to it are
made by the progress of research, but also because modifications in previously held views are frequently required. This
point needs no elaboration in the light of the recent history of physics, which has witnessed fundamental revisions
of theoretical assumptions that were once regarded as
indubitable. Nevertheless, to those whose notions of science have been formed within the intellectual framework
of classical rationalism, such revisions are often construed
as signs of the "bankruptcy" of modern science. A wholesale skepticism concerning the possibility of obtaining
genuine knowledge by way of science has in consequence
become widespread. In their quest for unshakable certainty, many have turned elsewhere for a type of knowl-

edge which the sciences do not provide, but which other modes of alleged knowing profess to supply.

There is another feature of modern scientific theory which calls for comment. The abstract formulations required to express the comprehensive conclusions of modern inquiry often make the relevance of those conclusions to the facts of gross experience far from evident; and the scientific objects postulated by current scientific theory seem to be not only utterly remote from the familiar things of daily life, but also to constitute an order of reality radically different from the reality of customary objects encountered in common experience. Everyone will doubtlessly recall the contrasting picture drawn by the late Sir Arthur Eddington between the ordinary table of common use and the scientific table. The former was described by him as extended, permanent, substantial, capable of supporting heavy objects, and possessing a great variety of esthetic qualities. The latter was characterized as being mostly emptiness, a congeries of rapidly moving and invisible electric charges separated by enormous relative distances, insubstantial, and possessing neither colors nor textures.

Given such an account of what are allegedly two tables, it is difficult to avoid raising the question, which of them is the "reality" and which the "appearance." Many scientists, including Eddington, have repeatedly raised it, in connection with physics as well as with other parts of scientific theory. Some have argued that our ordinary, common-sense encounters with the world yield only illusions, and that the objects discovered and formulated by theoretical physics are the exclusive reality. Others have maintained the contrary thesis, and have insisted that scientific theories are simply convenient fictions possessing no cognitive value. But whatever the answer proposed, the consequences of introducing such a distinction between the real and the apparent have been intellectually disastrous. For the supposition that such a distinction is relevant, has, in effect, alienated man from the rest of nature, and has reinforced a skepticism concerning the possibility of acquiring genuine knowledge about the world by way of the sciences. Despite the increased practical control over things which the advance of science yields, when that distinction is drawn the world is made progressively more mysterious and strange by the development of theoretical analysis. It is not surprising, therefore, that instead of becoming a source of enlightenment, the theoretical conclusions of science have frequently become means for strengthening the hold of ancient dogmas and for sanctioning the adoption of anti-rational philosophies of life.

The point of these remarks is that the conclusions of science are not fully intelligible without a clear sense of the logical relations in which they stand to each other as well as to the facts of gross experience, and without a clear conception of the intellectual method by which conclusions are certified as valid. A philosophy of science that undertakes a critique of the abstractions of science and that analyzes the nature of this method, therefore, seem to me indispensable, both for an adequate appreciation of the substantive content of science, as well as for a sober appraisal of the import of that content for the principles by which men order their daily lives.

This brings me to the third facet which science exhibits, namely, its method of inquiry. I have already noted that every special finding of science, whether it be general or particular in form, may require reconsideration because of fresh evidence that seems to challenge it. No question raised for study is ever settled beyond the possibility of its being reopened, for no proposed answer is indubitable. Indeed, when one surveys the history of science, the impermanence of nearly all of its comprehensive theories is most impressive. As I see it, it is the method of science that is relatively stable and permanent, rather than the answers to questions accepted at various times. It is certainly the case that the alleged certainty of scientific knowledge derives from the intellectual method by which the findings of inquiry are warranted.

To prevent misunderstanding, however, I must state explicitly that in my present usage, the word "method" is not synonymous with the word "technique." The technique of measuring wave lengths with a spectroscope is patently different from the technique of measuring the speed of a nerve impulse, and both are different from the techniques employed in assessing the date of composition of some historical document. In general, techniques differ with subject matter and may be altered with advances in technology. But the general logic of sifting and evaluating evidence, the principles employed in judging the adequacy of proposed explanations, the canons implicit in making responsible decisions between alternative hypotheses, are the same in all inquiries. These rules of *method* may be modified as science develops. Nevertheless, changes in them are usually infrequent and relatively minor, so that there is a recognizable continuity between the logic of proof used by scientists living at different times and places. It is these general principles of evaluating evidence that I have in mind when I speak of scientific method. Since in my view of it, the method of science is the most distinctive and permanent feature of the scientific enterprise, I propose to offer a brief account of some elements in that method.

It is appropriate to begin this account with the reminder that science is a social institution, and that professional scientists are members of a self-governing intellectual community, dedicated to the practice of modes of inquiry which must meet standards evolved in a continual process of mutual criticism. It is often supposed that the objectivity and validity of conclusions reached in the sciences are the products of individual intellectual insights, and of individual resolutions to believe only what is transparently true. Thus, the seventeenth-century philosopher and mathematician Descartes proposed a set of rules for the conduct of the understanding, adherence to which would guarantee that the mind would not fall into error. He stipulated that nothing is to be accepted as genuine knowledge which is not absolutely clear and distinct, or which is in the least manner doubtful. Descartes thereby assumed that scientific truth is simply the fruit of the operation of individual minds, each relying exclusively and separately on its own power to discover what is indubitable. Descartes' rules, however, are counsels of perfection, and have little effective value. Men are usually unaware of all the tacit assumptions involved in what they think is indubitable, and they frequently suppose themselves to be making no intellectual commitments of any kind, although in fact they are tacitly subscribing to much that is false. Accordingly, while pious resolutions on the part of scientists to be critical of their own assumptions may have a certain value, the objectivity of science is not primarily a consequence of such resolutions. On the contrary, assured knowledge in science is the product of a community of thinkers, each of whom is required by the tacit traditions of his group to be unsparing in his criticisms and evaluations of the cognitive claims presented to him.

It is through the operation of continual and independent criticism that scientific truth is achieved. The tradition of science is a tradition of toleration for new ideas, but a toleration qualified by a sturdy skepticism toward any notion which has not been subjected to observational and logical tests of validity—tests which are intended to be as severe as human ingenuity can devise. No one scientist engaged in this process of criticism is infallible, and each one will have his own peculiar intellectual or emotional bias. But the biases are rarely the same; and ideas which can survive the cross fire of the varied critical commentary that a large number of independently acting minds supply, stand a better chance of being sound than conceptions which are alleged to be valid simply because they appear to be self-evident to some individual thinker.

It follows that the source or origin of scientific ideas is entirely irrelevant in evaluating their empirical validity. The adequacy of scientific hypotheses is established ultimately by reference to matters capable of repeated public observation; and however great may be the honor and reverence scientists pay to the creators of scientific ideas and to the discoverers of new phenomena, it is not the individual authority of the great innovators which warrants the acceptance of their contributions. Moreover, there is nothing too sacred or too lowly, too unusual or too commonplace to be exempt from the critical scrutiny of science; and in this regard scientific inquiry is a respecter neither of persons, places, traditions nor questions. According to a well-known ancient story, a young student, once inquiring of his teacher what God was doing before Creation, was told that He was preparing hell for priers into mysteries. This answer illustrates an attitude which is radically incompatible with the tradition and temper of mind of modern science.

Nevertheless, despite its deliberate cultivation of a tough-minded critical spirit, the scientific attitude is not a wholesale skepticism concerning the possibility of genuine knowledge. On the contrary, the endless criticism in which the scientific community is engaged, is performed on the assumption that reliable knowledge *can* be achieved by way of just such a critical process. Indeed, reliable knowledge is in fact the product of science; and many of its conclusions, even when universal in scope, have stood up under centuries of severe testing. Although no conclusions of science are beyond the possibility of doubt, and all are corrigible in the light of future evidence, not all proposed conclusions of inquiry have to be abandoned as false. The fact that we *may* be in error, and that we must be ever on the lookout for discrepancies between our beliefs and what actually occurs, does not mean that we are always mistaken and that we know nothing.

But I must come to other phases of scientific method. According to a popular view, sometimes endorsed by distinguished scientists, science starts an inquiry by collecting facts, and then passes the data through some sort of logical sieve which yields a uniquely determined formulation of a regularity between phenomena. This is a seriously misleading account of what actually takes place. For inquiry begins with a *problem*, provoked by some practical or theoretical difficulty; and in general it is not easy to know just what facts one ought to gather to resolve the problem, or whether a purported fact really is a fact. Just what facts ought to be collected in studying the causes of rheumatoid arthritis? Is there really such a phenomenon as extrasensory perception, as many claim? The number of presumptive facts is legion, and we cannot note all of them. The scientist must therefore be selective, and concern himself only with those which are relevant. In consequence, he must adopt a preliminary hypothesis or guess as to how his specific problem may be resolved; and he must employ that hypothesis to suggest what he hopes are the relevant facts. In short, a responsibly conducted inquiry is guided by ideas that must be supplied by the investigator. Observation and experiment serve to test or control the adequacy of those ideas for the problem at hand; but observation and experiment do not provide the conceptions without which inquiry is aimless and blind.

It is a mistake to suppose, therefore, that the conclusions of scientific inquiry are uniquely determined by the facts of observation or experiment. In particular, it is of central importance to recognize that there is no logical route leading from data of observation to the explanations eventually adopted for them. As Einstein has repeatedly observed, the comprehensive theories of modern physics are "free creations of the mind," and require for their invention feats of imagination quite analogous to creative effort in the arts. Consider, for example, the motions of the planets, which have been observed for thousands of years. Neither the hypothesis that the planets move around the earth, as Ptolemy supposed, nor the hypothesis that they revolve around the sun, as Copernicus proposed, can be read off from what is directly observed.

Observations must be interpreted, and the interpretation involves the introduction of general ideas which are supplied by the creative imagination of the scientist. The common failure to recognize the role of this creative element in science is at the bottom of the charge, so frequently leveled against modern physical theories, that they are "unintelligible" because they are incompatible with "common sense"—that is, with ideas that are the deposit of a prior stage of scientific development, but which have become so familiar that they have assumed the status of necessities of thought. It is this failure also which is a partial source of the prevailing skepticism concerning science as an avenue to genuine knowledge. This skepticism has its roots in the naive assumption that certainty in knowledge is a matter of immediate apprehension or direct vision, so that the lack of self-evidence in the explanatory principles of science is taken as a mark of their fictional character.

Nevertheless, though scientific theories cannot be read off from the observed data, science is neither poetry nor pure mathematics, and the validity of a theory is established only through verifying it by experiment or observation. But a theory that is worth anything cannot be tested directly. Its consequences must first be explored with rigorous logic and eventually confronted with the outcome of controlled observations. Many students have argued, under the influence of the writings of Professor Bridgman, that all the notions which enter into a scientific statement, if the statement is to be meaningful, must be given explicit definitions in terms of what can be directly observed; and it is often maintained, especially by those concerned with less developed disciplines like psychology, that a proposed explanation of phenomena is to be rejected as meaningless if it contains terms for which operational definitions are not provided. These are, however, unduly severe requirements for scientific constructions, and little reflection is needed to realize that some of the most successful theories in the natural sciences do not satisfy them. For example, neither the term "electron" in current physical theory, nor the term "gene" in genetics are defined by way of an explicit operational procedure. It is therefore clearly not essential that the theoretical notions of a science should refer directly to matters identifiable in gross experience. Indeed, the explanatory power of theories is in general directly proportional to the remoteness of their key concepts from things capable of direct observation. What is essential, however, is that at some point in the deductive elaboration of a theory, suitable links be established between some of its concepts and experimentally identifiable properties of macroscopic objects.

It is for reasons just noted that deduction in general, and mathematics in particular, play such an important role in modern science. For mathematics is the great art of drawing rigorous conclusions from any set of clearly formulated postulates; and the significance of an explanatory theory can be determined only through the discovery, by way of deductive inference, of just what its principles do imply. It is an illusion to hold, however, as even distinguished physicists have sometimes maintained, that the mathematical language in which current physical theories are formulated shows that the structure of things is essentially mathematical and that therefore the world must have been created by a divine mathematician. The structure of processes in *any* world, whether actual or conceivable, could always be formulated in an appropriate mathematical notation. But the *postulates* of a theory about factual subject matter are not *mathematical* truths, anymore than is the statement that I possess two hands a mathematical truth. The postulates of a theory can be certified as valid, not by establishing their mathematical necessity, which is clearly impossible, but by showing that their logical consequences are in some measure in agreement with data of observation.

It is also frequently asserted that because of the introduction of quantitative distinctions and measurement, the natural sciences in effect ignore the diverse qualities of common experience, and fail to assign to the latter any place among the constituents of the world. How ill-founded such dicta are, is readily revealed by an analysis of the nature of measurement. Instead of ignoring or denying the existence of qualitative distinctions, techniques of measurement both presuppose qualitative differences as well as make it possible to recognize more subtle qualitative distinctions. A simple example will make this point clear. Human beings are able to distinguish between a certain number of degrees of warmth, and terms like "hot," "very warm," "warm," "lukewarm," "cool," and "cold" correspond to these familiar differences. But these differences were not ignored or denied when the thermometer was invented in the seventeenth century. The thermometer was developed when variations in experienced differences of warmth of many substances were found to be connected with changes in the relative volumes of those bodies. In consequence, variations in volume could be taken to represent changes in the physical state of a substance which in some cases correspond to the felt differences in their degree of warmth. It is possible, however, to recognize finer differences in variations of volume than in directly experienced changes in degrees of warmth; and there are extremes of heat and cold beyond which human beings are unable to discriminate any further, although volume changes beyond these limits can still be distinguished. It is therefore evident that the use of the thermometric scale does not involve ignoring qualitative differences; that scale merely orders qualities in an unambiguous manner, and provides a way of noting differences among them which would otherwise escape attention.

When the conclusions of the sciences are thus analyzed in the light of the logic of scientific procedure, it also becomes manifest that those conclusions do not assert that any of the objects or qualities of common experience are "unreal," and that when a theory succeeds in explaining the events around us, it does not explain them away. The occurrence of rainbows, for example, is explained in terms of the fundamental ideas of geometric optics. But it would be fatuous and self-stultifying to maintain as a consequence of this explanation that there are no such things as rainbows, or that only optical rays are "real" while the colors observed in definite patterns in the sky are "unreal." Indeed, no questions as to what is real or unreal can be significantly raised in such contexts. What the explanation achieves is the incorporation of the special phenomenon under investigation into a wider net of relations, so that the conditions for the occurrence of the phenomenon are shown to be similar to the conditions of occurrence of a large class of other phenomena as well. Again, when the macroscopic properties of a gas are explained in terms of the molecular theory of matter, so that in effect the laws of gases are "reduced" to theorems in the theory of statistical mechanics, this "reduction" cannot intelligibly be construed to deny that gases have temperatures, pressures, diffusion rates, and other properties. The reduction consists in exhibiting the regularities established for gases as special cases of more comprehensive uniformities, in terms of which many other special regularities can be shown to be systematically related. In short, the progress of science does not consist in the denial that the familiar faces of things are genuine phases or parts of existence. The progress of science consists in discovering connections and relations of order between things encountered in experience, thereby yielding intellectual, if not always practical, mastery over the events and processes of nature.

According to the well-worn cliché, we are living in an age of science. But the great hope, widespread before the first World War, in science as a force which would bring into being a humane social order and at the same time free men's minds from ancient superstitions, has noticeably weakened. Many men have turned away from the conception of reason embodied in the scientific process, and have come to place their faith in various forms of irrational philosophies of life as guides to salvation. There is no simple explanation for these changes in outlook, and I can mention only a few of the factors that have contributed to bringing them about. The cataclysmic wars and violent social upheavals of the past four decades have also weakened the appeal which the less dramatic ways of a cautious scientific intelligence once had. Those in seats of power, moreover, have not always been willing to use the knowledge and skills available to improve the estate of mankind throughout the world; and men who spend their lives in abject poverty and physical misery cannot be expected to wait indefinitely for the realization of dreams that are never implemented. Again, many of those who had pinned their hopes for mankind on the steady progress of scientific enlightenment undoubtedly expected too much too soon. In looking forward to the early embodiment of heaven on earth they were bound to be severely disappointed. Furthermore, the technological use of science in warfare, and the pseudoscientific conceptions with which various social movements have dressed up their policies, have persuaded many that science *per se* is not an unalloyed good but a potent source of evil. Scientists in their capacity as seekers after theoretical understanding have been held responsible for the barbaric uses to which modern society has put their discoveries.

There is one further reason for the decline of the great hope in science which seems important to me. This is the fact that, in the main, science has been taught, both on popular and advanced levels, either as a set of technologies or as a body of conclusions, without exhibiting them as products of the intellectual method which is the lifeblood of modern science and a supreme agent of liberal civilization. I am convinced that the general failure to present scientific conclusions in the light of the logic of scientific procedure is the source of much confusion and a cause of much contemporary obscurantism. For I am persuaded that a large potential audience is eager to learn just what is the import of recent theoretical researches for a vision of human life. The exclusive emphasis so often placed on applied science does not satisfy this interest. Man is among other things a speculative animal. If he does not obtain from scientists an adequate conception of the scheme of things entire and of man's place in it, he will turn to other sources, whatever be their credentials, for the materials for constructing such a vision. Scientists have done little to meet this legitimate need, in considerable measure because they are not trained to do so. Most scientists acquire the temper of mind and the intellectual method essential for competent research not by explicit formal teaching, but from example and by acquiring suitable habits of workmanship. Few scientists are vitally concerned with methodological issues, or with the logic of their discipline. When they do venture to discuss general ideas connected with their professional work, as they often do on ceremonial occasions, most of them usually repeat the uncriticized dubious philosophies they learned at their mother's knee.

I do not want to leave these comments entirely unsupported by evidence, and will therefore cite some misleading interpretations of natural science disseminated by leading scientists as well as philosophers.

Perhaps the most serious misinterpretation consists in the widely repeated claim that modern science is no longer "mechanistic," and that both the physical theory of relativity as well as quantum theory indicate the advent of a new scientific method which acknowledges the spiritual character of reality. Now it is indeed the case that the science of *mechanics*, which was once held to be the universal science adequate for explaining all processes in nature, has lost its pre-eminence; and no physicist today believes it is possible to understand the great variety of electrical and radiational phenomena in terms of the fundamental principles of Newtonian theory. But it is one thing to say that the science of mechanics is no longer regarded as the fundamental science, and quite a different thing to claim that science is in no sense any longer "mechanistic"—that is, that it no longer seeks to discover the mechanisms and the conditions involved in the occurrence of events and processes. Surely the latter is a grotesque claim, belied by every paper published in scientific journals. And just as surely, the recent recognition that mass is convertible under certain circumstances into energy, and that while the principle of conservation of energy has universal validity the principle of conservation of mass has only a qualified scope, does not signify that what is loosely called "matter" has disappeared from the universe or that some sort of "mental" stuff has taken its place. It is absurd to

31

suppose, moreover, that whenever some theory in a science is discovered to be inadequate for a given domain of phenomena, and is replaced by some other theory, a change in intellectual method of conducting inquiry is involved. Even a casual comparison of the logic of proof which dominated nineteenth-century physics and the logic which current science employs, makes abundantly clear that, despite alterations in the substantive concepts employed in the respective theories, there has been no change in the modes of evaluating evidence.

An analogous misconception has become current concerning the alleged "breakdown" of the principle of causality, because of the so-called "indeterministic" character of quantum theory. In particular, the famous Heisenberg Uncertainty Relations, derivable within that theory, have been hailed as establishing the "reality" of free will not only for human beings but also for electrons and other submicroscopic particles of physics. Now there is no doubt that quantum mechanics possesses features that sharply differentiate this theory in its internal structure from the theories of classical physics. For on one standard interpretation, quantum mechanics, unlike the theories which preceded it, is an essentially statistical theory, so that within the framework of this interpretation the theory establishes fixed connection only between *statistical* properties of aggregates, not between properties of the *individuals* which constitute those aggregates. But it is nonetheless doubtful whether this fact can be taken as evidence for the collapse of the causal principle, especially if the latter is construed (as it in fact must be, if it is to have a universal scope even within classical physics) as a methodological or formal principle rather than as a substantive one.

Within quantum mechanics itself, as has just been noted,

there are determinate and invariable relations between certain complex properties of things, even though no such relations are asserted to hold between other properties. Moreover, waving this point, quantum mechanics is so related to theories about macroscopic objects that in the limiting case, as the physical systems to which quantum mechanics is applied increase in their dimensions, quantum mechanics coincides with the theories of macrophysics. Accordingly, even if the submicroscopic particles do not satisfy what would be recognized as deterministic causal laws, it does not follow that *macroscopic* objects do not satisfy such laws. The supposition that quantum mechanics proves the general breakdown of causality is therefore a caricature of the actual situation. In any case, the ordering of our practical affairs, as well as the analysis of the extensive range of phenomena for which classical physics is still undoubtedly valid, can be successfully conducted only if we pay due heed to the fixed dependencies known to hold between events and the determinate conditions of their occurrence.

Moreover, an elementary confusion is committed when human freedom is construed in terms of the alleged "indeterminacy" of electrons and other physical particles. Human freedom is constituted by the capacity of human individuals to choose and act, when no external compulsions or constraints are present, in the light of their desires and the evidence available to them. It is a capacity which is fully compatible with either classical or quantum physics. Whether a human being possesses freedom in this sense can in general be ascertained by examining the circumstances of his overt behavior. The introduction into this context of considerations drawn from quantum theory is entirely irrelevant. Thus, before his imprisonment, Socrates was free to converse with the Athenian youth in the market place of ancient Athens; but after his condemnation by the Athenian court he was not free to do so. Neither the replacement of classical mechanics by quantum theory, nor the possibility that the latter may some day be succeeded by a strictly causal theory of radiation phenomena, in any way alters these facts.

There have also been persistent attempts in recent years to reintroduce organismic and teleological interpretations of all natural processes, inorganic as well as organic. Some of these attempts are based on representing current physical theory in terms of conveniently visualizable models, which are then described in anthropomorphic and highly misleading language. The old Bohr theory of atomic structure, for example, is usually presented as postulating a number of electrons revolving on definite orbits around a nucleus. According to this model, an electron may jump from one orbit to another, and so may either emit or absorb quanta of energy, provided that the second orbit is not already occupied by another electron. This supposition is then sometimes described as implying that, in leaving its original orbit, an electron must "know" in advance where its jump can terminate. Accordingly, atomic processes are said to be intelligible only in terms of teleological notions, essentially similar to those involved in accounts of human behavior.

More generally, it is frequently maintained that the motions and changes in nature are not "blind" and "purposeless," but that the universe is an "organism" whose parts are purposively related and exhibit modes of action quite analogous to those found in humans. Indeed, distinguished scientists and philosophers have sought to base their conception of a desirable society upon the assumed facts of subatomic structure; and some of them have even claimed that the thermodynamics of physical systems is evidence of the validity of Christian morals.

In my judgment, these various attempts to reinstate teleological notions into physical science are guilty of debasing and misusing language, in the interest of a spurious consolation which the use of such notions supposedly brings. To say that an electron must "know" into which orbit it will jump, is to use the word "know" in a sense radically different from its familiar connotation, with the misleading suggestion that there is some analogy, otherwise unspecified, between its familiar and its extraordinary meaning. Similarly, to declare that physical systems in general are purposively organized, either involves the use of the word "purposive" in a new but undefined sense, or it wipes out the manifest differences between animate and inanimate systems. Nothing but confusion is achieved when purely physical processes are formulated in language which is commonly used to characterize traits that are distinctive of human beings. The glaring differences between purely physical change and purposive human behavior are neither reduced nor illuminated by such descriptions. Modern physics has indeed discovered in the domain of the subatomic, hitherto unfamiliar types of structure and modes of organization; but when subatomic processes are characterized as forms of teleological behavior, language is being employed in a dangerously irresponsible manner. As the eighteenth-century Bishop, Butler, wisely remarked, "Things are what they are, and their consequences will be what they will be; why then should we desire to be deceived?"

I suspect that there is a will to illusion in all of us, and that we sometimes desire to be deceived. But I doubt whether the misconceptions I mentioned are, in general, the products of such a desire. On the contrary, I am of the opinion that most of the misconceptions concerning the content and import of science are in large measure the result of the pervasive failure to present science in a manner which makes explicit the logic of scientific method, the complex but flexible relations in which scientific abstractions stand to matters of gross experience, and the historical development of our efforts to understand the world around us.

To make these things explicit is the task of the philosophy of science, though whether this task is undertaken by the philosophical practicing scientist or the professional philosopher is of little moment.

The philosophy of science aims to effect both a systematic critique of scientific abstractions, and a comprehensive analysis of the components which enter the intellectual method by which reliable knowledge is acquired. It must therefore examine in detail the role of mathematical and other symbolical techniques in the construction of systems of explanation, and so help to identify what is conventional or definitional in the corpus of scientific statements, as distinct from what must be warranted by reference to empirical fact. It is of utmost importance to avoid the still widely prevalent confounding of statements which are expressions of laws of nature, and statements which are logically necessary but are without empirical content. For example, a moment's reflection suffices to show that the statement: "if no mammals are invertebrates, then no invertebrates are mammals" is not an expression of a biological law, since the statement can be certified as valid by means of purely logical operations. Nevertheless, comparable though more complex statements, expressing truths of logic but void of empirical import, have often been paraded as important conclusions of theoretical research in both the natural and social sciences.

A philosophic analysis of science also focuses attention on the various functions which theoretical constructions possess in inquiry, and thereby provides guards against the tempting fallacy of imputing meanings to statements which are irrelevant to the role those statements play in given contexts of usage. The philosophy of science also undertakes to evaluate the relative merits of alternate inductive policies, and to articulate the rational basis for the acceptance or rejection of proposed hypotheses about suspected regularities in nature. Moreover, it may attempt some form of synthesis of the special findings of scientific inquiry, either by constructing an inclusive account of the universe, or by formulating a set of basic categories into which everything that exists will supposedly fit—although in my opinion such attempts have been generally of dubious worth.

Finally, the philosophy of science may occupy itself with the relations of science and the rest of society. It may then examine the social determinants of scientific progress, the technological and ideational impact of scientific changes upon institutions and moral ideals, and the still unrealized possibilities for human betterment that are implicit in the funded scientific knowledge of mankind.

In any event, there is an imperative need for viewing science not simply as a set of technologies or as a body of conclusions, but as a continuing process of inquiry whose fruits are the products of a remarkable intellectual method. The need is imperative, if the age-old and socially costly conflict between the sciences and the humanities is ever to be overcome.

Interest in the humanities is sometimes associated with a snobbish traditionalism, a condescending attitude toward whatever is modern, and an ill-concealed contempt for rigorous, critical thought. There are in fact professed humanists who are lost in admiration for the sewage systems of the ancient Romans, but dismiss as beneath notice modern works of public hygiene. There are self-proclaimed humanists who are profoundly moved by the account in Herodotus of the heroism of the Greeks at Thermopylae, but regard as a sordid minor butchery of history the suppression of a tragically brave modern uprising against a cruel oppressor. There are humanists today who judge science to be an essentially menial occupation, and who see nothing but trivialities in current attempts at logical cogent analyses of the rationale of moral preference.

Nevertheless, those who exhibit these attitudes are not, in my judgment, the best representatives of the values for which "humanism" has long been a label. The passionate interest in whatever is human, whether it be a great work of imagination or a humble manifestation of man's feeling for his kind, as exhibited by such men as Leonardo, Erasmus, Spinoza, John Stuart Mill, or Santayana in our own day, is marked by no such narrowness of spirit or such intolerance of what is fresh and nascent. On the contrary, what is distinctive of humanism at its best is a judicious temper and balanced judgment, a disciplined readiness to profit from fresh experience, a broad angle of vision and avoidance of fanaticism, and a healthy scepticism toward what has not withstood the test of experience.

But if these are the traits essential for a genuine humanism, there can be no conflict between the scientific and the humanistic attitudes. For in their ideal form, a life devoted to science and a life devoted to the humanities exhibit a common temper of mind. There undoubtedly is an acute antagonism between many who pursue science and many who pursue the humanities—an incongruence which is in part the result of the extraordinary but inevitable specialization that has become so necessary for the successful pursuit of modern scientific inquiry, in part a fruit of the aloofness and analogous concentration that characterizes humanistic studies. But I venture the hope that this opposition can in considerable measure be mitigated, from one direction, at any rate, by exhibiting science as a form of activity which demands from those engaged in it the same kind of creative sensitivity, discriminating toleration, and reasoned understanding which humanistic studies at their best also require. Nor is it possible to dismiss the cardinal fact that the sciences, no less than the humanities, have much to contribute on the great issues which concern men as men. For the sciences provide the intellectual substance out of which we can construct an authoritative vision of nature and of man's place in it. Such a vision, based on the clearly and soberly understood findings of the sciences, may offer little comfort to those who are content with nothing less than a universe that is mindful of human needs. Nevertheless, such a vision has been in the past, and may once more become in the future, a source of spiritual strength and stability, and a dependable guide in the pursuit of reasonable human ends.

It must be both admitted and emphasized, however, that science does not exhaust the modes of experiencing the world. The primary aim of science is *knowledge*; and however desirable and precious this fruit of science may be, it clearly is not and cannot be a substitute for other things which may be equally precious, and which must be sought for in other ways. On the other hand, although what science has to offer is understanding, and although that understanding may be instrumental for gaining something else, knowledge is a final value, self-justifying because it enhances human power and feeds an enduring enjoyment. Science does satisfy what is perhaps the most distinctive human desire, the desire to know; and no one who is genuinely devoted to the humanities can ignore the dimension of experience to which science as the quest for knowledge is relevant. It satisfies that desire by dissolving as far as it can our romantic illusions and our provincialisms through the operation of a social process of indefatigable criticism. It is this critical spirit which is the special glory of modern science. There are no reasonable alternatives to it for arriving at responsibly supported conclusions as to where we stand in the scheme of things and what our destinies are.

THE APPLICATION OF PHYSICS
TO MEDICINE

By Norbert Wiener, Ph.D.

WE HAVE been used to a world dominated by Newtonian physics—a world of differential equations.
Speaking in a less mathematical way, it is a world in which,
given the position and momenta of all its particles in one
instant of time and the forces which apply to them, we can
extrapolate this world into the indefinite future, after the
manner in which the astronomer computes the nautical
almanac for many years ahead. It is a compact, tightly
organized world in which the whole future depends strictly
on the whole present. It is, in fact, so tightly organized that
the notion of cause and effect, which is our usual everyday
expression of the organization of the universe in time, is no
longer applicable. A textbook on classical celestial mechanics will in fact probably contain at no point the words
"cause and effect." If we ask, haltingly, "What is the cause
of an event, A?" classical Newtonian physics will tell us
that it is no less than the whole state of the universe at
some preceding instant. Such a comprehensive notion of
cause vitiates the entire concept.

Moreover, the classical Newtonian physics reads in the
same way forwards and backwards. The laws of Newton are
unchanged in the least if we change T, the ordinate of
time, into −T. The positions of the universe remain un-

touched by this transformation, and the velocities of the universe are simply reversed. Thus the computation of the nautical almanac backwards does not differ in any essential way from its computation forwards, and the problem of determining what eclipses took place in the days of the Babylonians is quite similar to that of determining what eclipses are to take place 5,000 years from now.

The vocabulary of medicine, on the other hand, ignores the universal tight process of classical physics, and uses the language of causality freely. A patient comes into a doctor's office: Some process, some phenomenon that takes place has gone amiss. Let us say that the processes of digestion do not behave in the way that they ought to. The doctor looks at the history of the patient, which is the record of what has happened to the patient in the past. He observes the disorders of process and makes a diagnosis. Let us say that there is an infection by some bacterium which is pouring into the blood substances which raise the temperature of the body and perhaps increase the rate of circulation, or prevent the digestive process from occurring as it should, or in some way alter the processes of the body so that they no longer fulfill a certain norm of what these processes ought to be.

On the other hand, the trouble may be hormonal, and the ductless glands are not pouring into the body substances needed for its ordinary metabolism, or are pouring these in at an abnormal rate. The determination of what is wrong is called the diagnosis. After the diagnosis, there follows the prognosis, or the prediction of how these processes will continue to go wrong if unchecked, and perhaps when and how they may lead to death, or the cessation of all vital processes. At the same time, the doctor is active therapeutically. He is introducing into the body new substances called drugs which will alter the function—*alias* metabolism—of the body in such a way as to change the abnormal—pathological—processes, and bring the behavior more nearly to the norm. The therapeusis may be surgical, and malfunctioning tissue may be removed or new connections introduced into the plumbing of the body which will have a similar effect in normalizing the functions.

This therapeusis in the case of psychiatry may be on a mental level, as indeed may be the malfunction which it is intended to remedy. The means here are different, as well as perhaps the disease. New elements are introduced into the patient's experience which may serve to alter the future course of his psychic and even his physical actions. Nevertheless, the main picture remains the same. We have an examination of the present functioning of the patient in the light of his past history; we have a diagnosis or characterization of the precise manner in which his functioning falls short of a desired norm; we have the prognosis, or the discussion of how this process may be expected to continue; we have the therapeusis, or the suggestion of some intervention which is intended to bring his activities near to the norm; and finally, we have a new prognosis in view of this intervention, which will anticipate what the new outcome is to be.

What I have given here is scarcely more than a sketch of the simplest form of activity of the doctor. This cycle of diagnosis and therapeusis may continue through many different stages. It does not, however, change its essential nature, and it is vitally dependent upon the notion of cause and effect, in a far more specific form than that used by the Newtonian physicist.

However, these notions are not confined to medicine. During the last war, the problems of technique of the soldier were in the process of being reduced to a very similar sequence. Let us suppose that we are discussing a national defense against air raids: For this purpose, we first need to know how air raids are being conducted and what their history was in the past. Here we have the elements of case history and diagnosis. We then extrapolate into the future and examine what the present program of air raids will produce in the course of time, or indeed, what any modified program would produce which is likely to be initiated by the enemy. This is the prognosis. We consider various sorts of countermeasures which involve the introduction of new antiaircraft arms, the distribution of antiaircraft batteries and the like, the possible relocation of our population and facilities of production, the improvement of our weapons, and the conditions under which these weapons should fire most effectively, both so as to bring down the enemy, and so as to give away as little as possible the secret of their location. This is indeed a form of therapeusis. It is followed by a new prognosis and a new and better therapeusis, until the situation is thoroughly in hand, or, at the worst, until we know that we are defeated. The whole attitude and psychology of this type of study, which is called operational research, is quite parallel to that of the doctor, even though it is likely to involve, besides doctors and military men in the classical sense, a large number of engineers, mathematicians, and physicists.

During and after the war, operational methods received a great deal of theoretical study as well as practical development. Lying behind them is an extensive use of the Theory of Probability, besides a new intellectual development due largely to John von Neumann, which is known as the Theory of Games. Here the process of war is assimilated not to medical treatment, but to a game such as chess, or bridge, or poker, and we take more specifically into consideration the fact that we are dealing not with a passive pathological process, but with an active enemy who can change his techniques, and indeed must change his techniques, so as to counter and render ineffective any methods of attack or defense which we may employ.

Indeed, this game element is not entirely missing in medicine. Pathogenic agents such as germs and viruses do not stay put and allow themselves to be passive victims of our new antibiotics and public health measures. It is well known that the use of penicillin and other such antibiotics has been rendered partly ineffective by the tendency of bacteria to mutate into antibiotic-resistant strains and perhaps even by the tendency of the human body to show ultimate changes acting in the same direction. The cleaning up of swamps may cut down the number of malaria-carrying mosquitoes, but may at the same time lead to agricultural and industrial changes which themselves have not negligible human effects. For instance, there may be places where we can only clean up swamps by cutting down our rice paddies and producing hunger. Again, the emphasis on one hormone in the diet may ultimately change our hormonal balance so that the need for another hormone, and indeed our tolerance for it, may be increased or decreased. The doctor confronts a multiform enemy which, even though it may not show a diabolical wish to exterminate us, may in the course of time show a new facet of its nature which amounts to a change of front in its attack, and may make it necessary for us to treat public health work as if it represented a continual war on an insatiable, purposeful enemy, at least to the extent that we must be aware of what measures such an enemy might use on us, and must often so frame our action as if we were confronted with such an enemy.

Thus, public health work and medicine in general participate in the nature of all operational methods, and demand operational research. There are, however, a large variety of other problems which have been consciously reduced to the same form during and since the war. Industrial competition is but a smaller and sometimes a more polite war. Even apart from competition, however, the industrialist must always face the problem of metabolic diseases in his own industry. A nationwide company must maintain inventories in a large number of warehouses. If these inventories are excessive, they will tie up capital which could be advantageously used elsewhere. If they are insufficient, this insufficiency will entail unfilled orders, with the loss not only of the profits to be expected from them, but of the good will needed for the company's continued existence, and this secondary loss may be as deadly as the penalty clause in an engineer's contract. How then should the warehouses be distributed, and what inventories should they carry in view of the actual business done by the company, its potential expansion or contraction, the nature of the market, and many other such considerations? This inventory problem is but one of the operational problems which are being effectively attacked by the means of the operational techniques developed in the war.

It would therefore seem as if medicine belonged to a new scientific category—that of operational science which is in sharp contrast with physics. Nothing could be further from the fact. Since 1900, there has been a revolution in physics, carrying it further and further away from the Newtonian point of view, and into closer and closer relation with modern operational theory which, as we have said, represents an extension of the point of view traditional in medicine. This revolution had a double origin, and on the strictly physical plane goes back to Boltzmann in Germany and to Willard Gibbs in the United States; whereas on the mathematical plane it goes back to Borel and Lebesgue in France.

I shall discuss this problem first from the point of view of Gibbs' work. Gibbs, that lonely beacon light of American science, spent the first few years of the present century, until his death in 1903, in founding what is now known as statistical mechanics. The thesis of this is that physics, even physics with Newtonian laws of motion, does not consist in taking a single system, subject to Newtonian laws, and following it through its development in terms of the Newtonian dynamics, but rather consists in starting with a set of such systems to which some notion of distribution or probability is applicable, and in following the changes of this distribution through their course in time. In the technical language of physics, such a distribution is called an *ensemble*.

Let us notice that the practical physicist always deals with ensembles rather than with single systems. No measurement can give a single physical quantity perfectly, nor in fact do anything more than give a very definitely limited degree of accuracy. To measure a position involves measuring it to the nearest centimeter, to the nearest tenth of a centimeter, to the nearest hundredth of a centimeter, and so on, but each step from one of the degrees of accuracy to the next is a new undertaking, and is in general about as difficult and time-consuming as the step before it. A physical measurement to one part in ten billion only involves ten of these steps, and is yet far more perfect than anything we find in practical physics. Thus, the final result of any physical measurement within the capacity of ourselves and our instruments is something covering a distinctly non-zero region, and the further history of the system involves the consideration of what will probably happen to a system whose initial coordinates are at some unspecified point in the system, having at best a specified distribution. This distribution will be wide where our measurements are inaccurate, or where we meet important, unknown disturbances of the system from outside, and will be narrow when our data are accurate and our system is very well isolated and insulated.

Newton himself was largely concerned with what is perhaps the most perfectly insulated system known to physics: the system of the finite number of nearly rigid bodies constituting the solar system, together with their relative motions and their revolutions. It is true that such a system is immersed in our galactic universe with which it interacts by light, both visible and invisible, as, for example, by radio waves. However, starlight is but a feeble thing, and its action on the sun and the planets, particularly its gravitational action, is quite negligible. I do not know whether the pressure of starlight may or may not give a barely observable push to the highly dispersed matter forming the tail of a comet, but I doubt very strongly whether this is noticeable compared with the push coming from the light of the sun. On the other hand, while the planets are not perfectly rigid bodies, and while this departure from rigidity does have a cumulative effect known, after the writings of Sir George Darwin, as tidal evolution, this effect, which has brought the moon always to present one face to the earth and will ultimately cause the moon to fall back into the earth, important as it is even over geological ages, is of very slight importance when it comes to the prediction of the nautical almanac from year to year, or its analogous extension into the past. Newton's rigid dynamics was thus first applied in the field in which departures from its logical rigidity, although philosophically important, were of the smallest numerical and practical significance.

This insulation of a dynamical system which comes about naturally in the celestial mechanics of the solar system is the hardest of all things to obtain in an experiment on earth. Before we have a collection of particles of possible systems which has been adequately combed out for uniformity in that initial position and momenta, we must go through a complex of preparatory stages which is known as *collimation*. Collimating a system is a process which we can illustrate by the biological analogue of a number of rabbits which we are preparing for an experiment in psychology. These rabbits, carefully picked for their size, health, and genetic constitutions, are put in boxes until they have become evenly accustomed to the environment and are then released. We observe how and when they run away, and what paths they follow. This is an experiment which is intimately connected with the direction of time, and cannot be effectively reversed. To reverse the experiment would involve the leaving of open boxes where rabbits could spontaneously run into them, and then the combing out of this class of rabbits, moving freely and without interference, by some process occurring after their capture. It is familiar to all of us that not enough rabbits run into such boxes to give us an adequate population to study, and that the whole idea of an experiment reversed in time partakes of the nature of the efforts of the aged man in *Through the Looking Glass*, who spent his time searching through the grass for wheels of hansom cabs.

Thus, in fact, scientific experiments deal with populations or ensembles of experiments which are in the hands of an observer who can act forward in time, but not backwards. Furthermore, before such experiments can be carried out, there must be certain types of assumptions which are never completely verifiable. It is essential to the existence of any physics that there should be laws of nature, even though they may be only statistical laws of nature, which bind the whole future and are not subject to arbitrary revisions or revocation by some mundane congress. To appeal once more to that scientific author, Lewis Carroll, there can be no science in a world like the croquet game in *Alice in Wonderland*, in which the balls are hedgehogs which get up and walk around, the mallets are flamingoes of a peculiarly intractable nature, the hoops are card soldiers who persist in moving from one side of the field to the other, and the rules are made on the spur of the moment by the arbitrary and uncontrolled decree of the Queen. Even such apparent exceptions to the complete statistical lawfulness of nature as the expanding universe of Hubbell and Lemaitre conceal an assumed lawfulness behind them, and probably do not amount to much more than the choice for a time variable of some quantity other than the natural one with respect to which the laws of science are invariant.

Thus the world of modern physics consists in a statistical distribution of systems attached to a probability which is constant in time and which is such that time itself is nothing more than a level picking out one of the natural probability-preserving transformations which the system undergoes in its own history. Of these transformations, it is only those which go in the particular direction from past to future which are accessible to physics, so that we are only dealing with about one half of the set of all transformations in time reaching both to the past and to the future.

This world with which modern physics deals is precisely analogous to, and even identical with the world of operational methods. Modern physics falls neatly into a category whose earlier embodiments are to be found more in medicine than in the physics of Newton.

The concept of such a world in physics was the brilliant work of Willard Gibbs of Yale, who was so much of a hermit that he was almost unknown during his lifetime on his own campus. Gibbs' primary idea was that for certain very important sorts of dynamical systems, the set of states which they occupied as an ensemble for a given energy level, and over which there existed a certain probability distribution, was retraced in time with the evolution of the system in such a way that regions equally probable in phase were equally distributed in time. This notion, which has proved to be one of the most fertile of modern physics, was thoroughly understood by Gibbs in its implications, but was thoroughly beyond his access by means of the tools available to him, not only in its proof, but even in its very statement. What Gibbs does with this notion in a general physical-philosophical way is right and brilliant, but the specific things he says concerning it are false and nonsensical. It took physics perhaps twenty years to begin to catch up with what Gibbs had outlined, and to use correct and rigorous mathematics to state and to prove it.

It is one of the many ironies of the history of science that the main notions needed for the rigorous presentation of Gibbs' ideas had been developed by French mathematicians even before his death. The two very different men who were responsible for this were the late Henri Lebesgue, and Emile Borel. The notions which were needed to supplement the work of Gibbs were those of the Lebesgue measure and the Lebesgue integral.

For many years before the beginning of the century,

the notion of measure of sets of points did not go very far beyond the interior of smooth curves. There were parts of mathematics which had already shown the need for much more radical concepts. Chief among these was the theory of trigonometric series in which Emile Borel was interested, as indeed he was interested in all branches of analysis. Emile Borel is a remarkable man. There is scarcely any field of mathematics in which his influence is not visible, but there are very few branches of mathematics in which the principal theorems bear his name. A young French mathematician has told me that he considers him one of the really great names of mathematics who has been cheated from the full meed of his recognition by the fact that he is "*flou*," or rather soft and negligent in developing the full consequences of his own concepts. He is one of the great names in probability theory, and he was certainly aware of a new ferment which the statistical mechanics people had set to work in probability theory and in physics.

He spent some years just before 1900 in trying to develop a new and more adequate theory of integration and measure. He made some progress in this direction, but it is quite clear that his work only represented an intermediate stage of progress, and it was left to another to put a definitive seal upon it. This other person was his old pupil, Henri Lebesgue. My French friend has described Lebesgue to me as a very great mathematician, but two-dimensional where Borel was three-dimensional. He was a purist in mathematics and devoid of interests outside of mathematics, and more particularly, in physics. He never took the slightest step to make a physical application of his new integral, nor did he display the least interest when others did so.

The fact is that the Lebesgue integral was not only a

language in which Gibbs' ideas could be expressed and in which the theorems necessary to justify his work could be proved, but that it was in essence the only such language. Borel already showed a certain awareness of this around 1912, when he used the concepts of the Lebesgue integral to underline the inadequacies of Gibbs' own statement of his problem. After that, the war produced a gap, and the first paper which I believe to have combined the Gibbsian physics and the Lebesgue integral was one of my own dating from 1920, and concerned with the mysterious dance of suspended particles in a liquid which is known as the Brownian motion. Even this paper, however, was little understood at the time of writing and did not lead directly to the general use of the Lebesgue integral in statistical mechanics. This latter consummation did not take place until about 1930, when the late George David Birkhoff of Harvard produced a theorem concerning the Lebesgue integral which was obviously the true ergodic theorem needed for the justification of Gibbs.

Even before the proof of the Birkhoff ergodic theorem, however, a new branch of physics, quantum mechanics, was fundamentally bound to the study of a certain space in which the Lebesgue integral was central. This space, the so-called Space of Hilbert, introduced the Lebesgue integral in terms of the other use of Lebesgue integration to which Lebesgue himself was devoted: that for the extension of the theorem for trigonometric series. From the beginning, this quantum mechanics was developed to overcome certain difficulties which Newtonian mechanics had shown. Instead of being a theory of complete determinism, it was a theory into which the notion of probability entered at the very beginning. It has recently become possible for me to show that this theory is in fact an example of a

Gibbsian theory in which, however, the development of a single set of observable initial conditions is not Newtonian and unique in all possible variables.

Thus it is not wrong to say that the present physics has assumed an aspect much more compatible with the traditional one of medicine than seemed possible half a century ago. Conversely, the methods of modern physics are having a back effect on medicine. There are certain medical phenomena of a highly numerical and quantitative nature which seem particularly adaptable to the application of the new mathematical-physical techniques. Among these are the varying action potentials in the brain which record themselves as the so-called electroencephalograms. These represent sequences of phenomena taking place in time, and distributed in space over different parts of the brain. They seem to be closely connected with the statistical theory, central in operational analysis, which we call prediction theory.

The brain potentials are subject to oscillations which are shown in electroencephalograms. These have already been of some service in the study of epilepsy and other neural conditions, and have clearly not been exhausted as a tool for the study of brain physiology and pathology. Conspicuous among the oscillations found in the electroencephalograms are certain ones whose period is about one ninth or one tenth of a second. These are known as the *alpha rhythm*. Work done jointly by the Massachusetts Institute of Technology and the Massachusetts General Hospital is now showing that if my methods of serial analysis are applied to the study of alpha rhythm, it often proves to be not a mere fortuitous assemblage of oscillations of a frequency not far from nine or ten per second, but an organized phenomenon which retains a memory of its own phase for as long as one or two seconds. The mathematical methods for studying this consistency in phase must be implemented by electrical apparatus already in use, and the general theory of what we are doing bears a close logical relation to the work of Michelson on the interferometer. It will be recalled that by letting two rays of light interfere with the aid of this apparatus, one obtains a series of circular fringes, and that the number of such fringes which can be observed from the inside and before they extinguish one another is a measure of the purity of the spectrum of the light employed. It will be remembered also that the use of this apparatus on light coming from mirrors at a distance of several hundred feet enabled Michelson to perform a task never before successfully undertaken: to measure the disks of some of the fixed stars. This triumph of delicate technique is now finding its counterpart in the examination of the alpha rhythm, where we are discovering a degree of consistency which leads to precise and previously unhoped-for numerical determinations which, in my opinion, cannot help leading to new studies of the utmost physiological and pathological importance.

Furthermore, the study of such series in time can be associated with a comparison of waves from different parts of the brain by which we can determine which part of the brain is driving which, as far as the alpha rhythm is concerned. It is not unnatural that physical methods which are based on probability and on concepts which allow different degrees of causality, as opposed to the universal rigid determination of Newtonian physics, should be useful in studying physiological and pathological phenomena of cause and effect.

Closely associated with operational analysis and synthesis is the notion of *feedback*. In pointing a gun at an airplane, we read the difference between the expected position of the missile and the expected position of the target, and we use this quantity as a new datum to be fed into our control apparatus in such a manner as to bring the shell nearer to the plane. This type of control is closely related to that process discovered by Claude Bernard and later studied by Cannon, which has received the name *homeostasis*.

It is well known that life cannot exist except within narrow ranges of temperature conditions, chemical conditions, and the like. These conditions are maintained in the body by well-known but only partly understood internal apparatus not unlike the feedback which operates the temperature control in a room by means of thermostats, and keeps the temperature substantially constant. The theory of such control apparatus is now an established science on the engineering levels and, operationally speaking, we are learning to recognize not only the physiology of such performance, but also its pathology. This knowledge of the pathology of inadequate homeostasis is already beginning to give us interesting results in medicine.

For example, in the somewhat cancer-like disease of the blood known as leukemia, Dr. Paul Hahn and myself have been able to show that the numerical course of the increase of leukocytes in the blood indicates not merely that the production and destruction of leukocytes have gone wild, but that in this abnormal and deadly behavior, they still show a regularity of relationship to one another which indicates not the absence of a control mechanism, but a valid control mechanism which is operating at a wrong level. What consequences this observation may produce in the future treatment of leukemia we do not know, but it is manifestly a consideration to be kept closely in mind.

Again, cancer itself, which has already been suspected to be a leukemia-like phenomenon, is beginning to have some light thrown on it. In cancer, a process not unrelated to the normal regenerative activities of the body has gone wild and whatever controls the process ordinarily fails to work as it should. The most conspicuous example of regeneration in the adult human being is the regeneration of liver tissue after some of it has been removed. According to the studies of Drs. Child, Barr, Holswade, Harrison, and others, it is now quite clear that this regeneration is controlled in the healthy individual by a factor, very likely of an enzymatic nature, which reduces the regeneration and terminates it when sufficient tissue has been regenerated. If this homeostatic factor were not active, it is quite conceivable that liver regeneration might go on in an uncontrolled cancerous form, and might lead to the death of the individual. In the study of both the nature of the controlled factors and of the quantitative way in which they operate, the studies of feedback, which have already been made by engineers rather than by doctors, bid fair to be of the greatest importance.

Any paper on a rapidly growing subject must be tentative. My sole claim here is that the methodological gap which has existed for so many years between medicine and other biological sciences on the one hand, and physics on the other, is rapidly being narrowed. How far it can be narrowed, and how fruitful the new notions may be expected to prove in that most important part of medicine which is an art rather than a science, I cannot here pretend to say. However, I am very hopeful of the outcome.

THE BEARING OF
ANTHROPOLOGY
UPON MEDICINE

By Benjamin D. Paul, Ph.D.

THE DRAMA of disease and healing is always played
out on three stages—the somatic, the psychological,
and the cultural. We know a good deal about conventional
or somatic medicine; we are learning quite a lot about
psychological medicine; but as yet we are only dimly aware
of the cultural component in health and illness. Let me
illustrate the role of the cultural component by citing a
recent occurrence.

One day a South African physician working in a Zulu
area was called into the country to see an ailing old man.
Examination revealed a serious apical cavity of the lung.
It was not at all certain that the patient would survive, but
the physician urged that members of the family come to
his office to receive drugs that might assist recovery. They
never came. Instead, as the physician later learned, they
called in a native diagnostician, a woman "witch doctor."
She found that the illness was due to witchcraft perpetrated
by the old man's son and daughter-in-law. To remedy
matters the indignant father evicted the couple from his
household and took steps to disinherit his son.

The physician was distressed by news of this unfortunate

turn of events; about a month after his visit to the Zulu home, he initiated inquiries, half fearing that the old man would have succumbed to severe tuberculosis. The physician was surprised and chagrined to find out that the witch doctor's intervention had apparently proved effective—the patient was back on his feet and doing well. This unexpected outcome prompted the physician to uncover the history of the whole case. This is what he found:

The patient was a self-respecting Zulu patriarch whose eldest son had died, making the second son his effective heir. But the latter turned out to be a wastrel. The eldest daughter assumed many of the family's financial responsibilities, in this respect assuming the role properly assigned to the eldest son in a patrilineal society where women occupy a lower social standing. She went to the city to work, bringing home money to help her father accumulate cattle, symbols of honor and prestige and objects of fond attention among the Zulu.

The ne'er-do-well son spent money in the city rather than earn it. On returning to his father's home he would demand that cattle be slaughtered for a feast to honor the heir, according to custom. The father was reluctant to do this; his sympathies were with his daughter whose earnings had bought the cattle and who objected to the selfish demands of her arrogant brother. The son, knowing that tradition was being flouted, talked to the neighbors who put pressure on the father to abide by tradition. The father resisted.

One day the son compounded injury by marrying a townsgirl of dubious status, bringing her to live in the house of his father, in accord with patrilocal custom. He even prevailed upon the father to part with eleven head of cattle in exchange for the bride, overriding the protest of his daughter. Repeatedly torn between the demands of tradition and the continuing protests of his devoted daughter, the old man was subject to continuing psychological stress. The daughter-in-law quarrelled and came to blows with her sister-in-law. The pay-off came when she committed the unthinkable act of spitting in the face of her father-in-law. It was at this point that the old man became very ill and called in the public health doctor.

In his diagnosis, the doctor discovered the hole in the lung but missed the rest of the picture. The "witch doctor" who came after him saw the social and psychological factors, missing the hole in the lung, but coming closer to a complete diagnosis of the patient's trouble. We can now appreciate the combination of somatic features (a lesion in the lung), psychological features (conflict and anger and anxiety), and cultural forces (norms of father-son relationship and marriage patterns) that conspired against the Zulu patriarch. The prescription that the troublesome couple be evicted was effective medicine cloaked in the culturally acceptable trappings of witchcraft accusations.

The parallels in our own society are clear. Despite superficial differences, our body and the Zulu body are virtually the same. The same basic psychological mechanisms are at work in all humans. The essential distinction is that American culture differs from Zulu culture. We have different expectations, different ways of viewing the world. What an American experiences as stressful may not be stressful to a Zulu and *vice versa*. These are the things that anthropology tries to study. How and why are the ways of the Zulus different from those of Americans and other people? In what respects are they alike? What is the relationship, if any, between race and language and culture? And how do all these combine to affect behavior in general and health behavior in particular? These are some of the questions that anthropology seeks to answer.

The concept of culture can be easily misunderstood. We all know the word "culture" but it means various things to various people. In any society the experience of being ill or recovering, of being a patient or a therapist is heavily affected by the meanings we attach to these experiences. The meanings, in turn, are influenced by the particular cultural system in which doctors and patients perform their roles, whether in Zululand or in New York City. Suffering, convalescing, curing, are forms of behavior regulated, like all human behavior, by a set of meanings defined by the cultural environment in which one lives. From this it follows that medicine, whatever else it may be, is part of culture. The more we can learn about culture, the more we will know about medicine.

Culture is something so much upon us, so essential to daily existence, that it is difficult to see. It is taken for granted like the air about us. We could see culture if we could somehow step out of our cultural vestments—if we could step back and view it from a distance. This perspective is difficult to achieve. Anthropology tries to gain this perspective by backing off in three directions as it were—in time, that is, comparing early phases of culture with later phases; in space, or comparing the culture of one people with that of another group elsewhere in the world; and finally, by comparing human behavior with the behavior of other animals.

Let me begin with the last of these three methods of grasping the concept of culture. Some animals live solitary lives. Some, including humans, are social animals. An interesting comparison can be made between insect society and human society. Some social insects practice a kind of

Benjamin D. Paul

agriculture; they shred leaves and prepare underground beds in which they raise a food crop of mold-like fungi or headless mushrooms. They fertilize their gardens with the excrement of caterpillars or with their own night-soil. Some insect colonies keep dairies consisting of plant lice which they house in special barns, "milking" them for their honeydew, and putting them out to pasture. Some insect communities warehouse their food, keeping a season's supply of honeydew milk or gathered seeds. They process their food, milling their grain with powerful jaws. Some social insects practice drainage to divert water into prepared channels and away from their nests. Some keep pets, such as beetles, for pleasure or other purposes. Some have a sanitary corps to keep the colony clean. Some have nursery and child-care services. Some have offensive armies to capture, plunder, and enslave.

The general similarities between insect society and human society are quite apparent. Both live collectively, exhibit a marked division of labor, and have specialized occupations which are integrated for the common good. Relative harmony prevails within particular communities and conflict often occurs between communities.

The differences, however, are more instructive. Taking ant society, for instance, I may cite four contrasts between humans and social insects. The first difference is that ant society is dominated by females. This isn't an important point for present purposes and perhaps the difference is not really so great as it might appear at first glance.

Secondly, occupational specialization is characteristically achieved in insect society by means of organic or somatic specialization. Thus warriors among social insects do not have armor or guns; instead they develop massive heads for ramming the enemy or protecting the nest. Some ants have enormous jaws instead of machines for grinding grain. Others become honeypots, their abdomens swelling prodigiously as they hang from the ceiling and receive supplies brought in by industrious companions. In contrast, man achieves specialization by means of learning and training, rather than bodily developments; he makes a tool rather than becoming a tool.

The third difference is that in ant society childhood is relatively brief. Perhaps only five per cent of the life span of an ant is spent in growing up; about twenty-five percent of a typical human's life is spent in maturing. In the case of the ant, the brevity of youth is apparently functional. Adult members of the colony waste a minimum of time on feeding and tending the immature. The young become useful rapidly, helping the whole colony survive. This contrasts sharply with the situation among humans, and it relates to the fourth and most important difference between the two kinds of societies.

The signals for running a complex insect society are largely contained in the genetic make-up of the individual. The system for organizing insect society, for guiding the members to coordinate their efforts, is transmitted mainly by biological inheritance. In distinction, the signals for regulating human society are largely transmitted independently of man's genetic structure. They are transmitted by means of teaching and learning. I use learning in a broad sense to include not only formal schooling, but also conscious and unconscious inculcation and imitation. In this process of social transmission—a process sometimes called socialization or enculturation—the new generation learns to become human, to have the qualities and skills and manners and interests and values that make him a fit and functioning member of his particular social group.

The sum total of what one generation transmits socially to the next generation is that complex thing we call the "culture" of the group.

This then is the crux of the difference between ant society and human society: whereas both live in a society and thus differ from solitary animals, the blueprint for the perpetuation of an ant society is essentially contained in hereditary or biological mechanisms (loosely called "instincts"), while the blueprint for the perpetuation of a human society is essentially contained in the culture of the group, in its social rather than biological heritage. In short, men have culture, ants have not.

We may now see one of the virtues of prolonged maturation in humans. Culture must be acquired after birth; instincts are acquired before birth. It takes considerable time to incorporate the particular standards of one's culture, including the indispensable set of symbols we call language. A prolonged period of plasticity and dependence on parents and elders enables society to transmit its culture from one generation to the next.

Consider this dramatic difference between a society run by instinctual mechanisms and one regulated by culture. If all ants of a given species were effaced, except for a single fertilized female, this lone survivor could rapidly reproduce the entire society, which would function in the same smooth and complex manner as before. But if all humans were destroyed, except for one couple sound in body but somehow innocent of culture, no such restoration of the pre-existing form of society would occur. The whole of man's laboriously built culture, developed in the course of more than one half million years of history, would be lost; at best, it could be painfully re-invented only during the course of untold centuries. Unlike the color of his eyes or the color of his skin, man's culture is not imprinted in his chromosomes.

It may seem that culture is a precarious means for sustaining the present forms of human society; it may seem miraculous that the thread of cultural continuity has never been snapped in man's long ascent from the simian state. Yet reliance on culture, rather than on biological mechanisms exclusively, gives man obvious advantages. It gives him a high degree of adaptability. If waging war is part of a people's way of life, for example, this disposition can be eliminated without necessarily killing the society or the individuals. In contrast, warring ants remain warring ants, and only eradication of the species will eradicate their inclination to make war. Each species of social insect has its peculiar form of society. Conversely, different forms of insect society are sustained by different biological species. But the world of contemporary man comprises only a single biological species; the "races" of man are but variations within the species. Although belonging to the same species, different groups of humans have evolved different forms of society, each characterized by a different culture.

The fact that cultural patterns are more malleable than genetic patterns does not necessarily mean that culture is susceptible to rapid transformation. All the cultures now existing are the products of thousands of years of experience, mostly by trial and error. No culture is completely static, but, for the most part, change is gradual and imperceptible. Very little of cultural alteration is planned or intentional. Individuals do modify the culture in which they live but the reverse influence, the impact of the cultural system upon the individuals, is much more decisive and emphatic.

The process of culture change can be better appreciated by focusing attention on language. English and German were once one language. As groups of speakers became separated, the constant unnoticed changes that are always creeping into language wedged the two tongues apart to the point where each is now foreign to the other. The diverging process continues within different regions of the United States, creating dialects which eventually could become distinct languages if communication barriers sprang up between the regions. Now this does not happen according to plan; it just happens. The unpremeditated changes in language turn out to be systematic. Although language is a part of human behavior, it seems to have a direction and momentum of its own when we inspect its course over a span of several generations of speakers. Language is part of culture, it is a product of culture, and it is a vehicle for the transmission of culture. What is true of linguistic change applies also to cultural change in general.

I have noted one important source of linguistic change: variation and drift. A second important stimulus to change is the impact of another language. Thus modern French is a derivative of Latin showing the impact of Celtic; the English language shows the impact of Norman French. Thirdly, language can be changed by deliberate effort. Lewis Carroll successfully coined the word "chortle"; others have deliberately introduced similar new elements into our language. Deliberate effort is the least effective of the three mechanisms that make for change in language or culture.

One form of deliberate effort is directed culture change. Many programs of health improvement are in fact instances of directed culture change. This is particularly true of health education campaigns here and abroad. Since conscious effort is but one of three forces operating on the culture of a group, those who are concerned with health promotion would do well to bear several things in mind. In the first place, cultural patterns tend to change slowly. An illusion that evidence or persuasion will bring about rapid changes in group habits and group ideas can lead to premature disillusion. Americans are particularly subject to this kind of disappointment since American culture places so high a value upon innovation for its own sake. We are inclined to assume that any change is for the better and that if something hasn't changed much, it must be out of date and undesirable.

In the second place, cultures are intricate designs for group living, slowly fashioned, each part standing in some organized relationship to the other parts of the cultural totality. Culture, like language, has order and structure. Therefore, a change in one aspect of a culture may cause unforeseen effects in other parts of the same cultural system. A specific example will show the interlocking nature of the parts that make up the culture of a people.

In parts of India well-inspired efforts to increase food production have actually resulted in decreased production because of certain social and cultural consequences that were not part of the plan. Land reforms were instituted with the twofold aim of augmenting over-all agricultural productivity (thus improving health and living standards) and reducing the economic inequality between land-poor and land-rich families. A common feature of the land reform program has been a limitation on the amount of land that any family is allowed to own. This regulation has accelerated the breakup of the Indian joint family. Separated, the component elementary families are allowed more land than they would possess living together as one family unit.

The joint family has long been the accepted form in rural India, sanctioned in scripture and ancient law. Typically, it consists of a father and his sons, or a set of brothers, and their respective wives brought in from the outside, as well as their children; it is an aggregate of two or more nuclear families. This social cluster acts as a single consumption unit, with a common kitchen and a common purse. It is also a single production unit, all members working the land which they hold in common under the trusteeship of the ranking male, although each man is entitled to his share of the joint family property should he leave the common household. Joint families regularly undergo a process of alternating formation and fission. The marriage of sons expands the group but when the total reaches an unwieldy number, fission sets in. Separation of units can occur when the father dies and the married sons fall out, or when these sons die and the married men are related to each other only as cousins. They may blame their wives for their troubles, saying that they are obliged to set up separate homes to avoid domestic strife, each man keeping his parcel of land. Later the process of accretion starts again and so it goes, or so it has gone in the past.

At present fission is outrunning formation. Households are getting smaller, partly due to the new land measures which work hardships on extended families. Peasant families in India still convene for ceremonial purposes but they are ceasing to function as production and consumption units. It happens that the joint family is often a more efficient arrangement for agricultural production than are the several nuclear families working their lands independently. Some tasks, such as guarding the ripening crops against animal and human predators or harvesting the yield, require attention night and day during critical seasons. Large families can supply more field hands at one time, or successive shifts of workers. They are also in a better position to raise capital for animals and equipment. Thus one of the unforeseen consequences of land reform has been a decline in agricultural efficiency through speeding up the fission of the joint family.

Of course, this may prove to be but a short-term effect. Eventually the small family may prove itself superior in rural India; at this point it is difficult to say. Nor does this reverse effect obtain in all parts of India. However, the lesson to be learned is that an outcome such as this might have been anticipated and programs might have been better planned if more attention had been paid to the facts of local culture and the prevailing modes of social organization and economic cooperation.

The phenomenon of cultural dislocation is paralleled in the realm of ecology. There is the classic case of the duck farmer who was bothered by skunks. He succeeded in killing off the skunk population, but was dismayed to see his duck population dwindling as well. He didn't realize that skunks eat the eggs of snapping turtles which eat ducklings. Fewer skunks resulted in more turtles and fewer ducks. The farmer was unaware of a critical link in the ecological chain. The farmer's plan to rid his place of skunks was based on insufficient knowledge of the ecological balance wheel which, like the submerged snapping turtles themselves, can operate below the surface of ordinary human awareness. Let me document another ecological upset more directly concerned with human health.

When the Dutch were in Sumatra, they discovered that beriberi was due to nutritional deficiency. Reliance on polished rice was partly responsible for the deficiency. Rice is polished in order to preserve it; unpolished rice attracts beetles, complicating the storage problem. To conserve the health of their laborers, the Dutch owners of tobacco estates, finding it difficult to have natural rice shipped in (this was during the first world war), decided to grow their own rice. This they managed to do, remedying the scourge of beriberi but at the cost of attracting mosquitoes to the new rice swamps, thereby introducing malaria. This example relates to health and illness but concerns the domain of ecology more than the province of culture. Let me now give you an example of planned action which deals with both health and culture.

Milk supplements were introduced to school children in a rural Peruvian area. Health authorities counted the program a success since it was known that milk contained nutritive elements in which the children were deficient and since administrative records indicated that milk was being consumed in good quantity. But this wasn't the whole story. Closer inspection by an anthropologist on the scene revealed that people in one of the villages concerned did more than merely reconstitute the milk before drinking it. They boiled the milk. This was unnecessary as a sanitary measure. However, boiling milk is a long-established practice in this area where all foods are classified as either "hot" or "cold." According to their cultural beliefs, milk was a "cold" substance that had to be heated before it was fit for consumption. The question of sterilization, in our sense of the term, was not involved. To heat the milk, they had to have fuel. To get fuel, schoolteachers had to send out the children to scour the vicinity for wood, a scarce commodity in that area. Classes were called off for this purpose. Nor would children drink the milk without flavoring it. Milk just wasn't regarded as a valid drink by itself. It had to be flavored by adding cinnamon or chocolate. Unflavored milk is disagreeable by their esthetic and cultural judgment, just as some New Yorkers consider clam chowder unpalatable without tomato flavoring. Incidentally, the American passion for chilled drinks contrasts not only with preferences in rural Peru, but with the taste of many Europeans. American hotels often have a separate tap for ice water which most Frenchmen, for instance, consider superfluous.

Reverting to the Peruvian instance, only some children drank milk as part of their school lunch, those whose parents could afford to send along the indispensable chocolate or cinnamon to provide flavor. Thus the poorest children who most needed the nutrients supplied by the supplementation program were least benefited. In sum, a program that seemed quite satisfactory on the basis of administrative reports did, in fact, have two unforeseen consequences: loss of school time to gather wood for heating the milk and failure of the poorest children to take advantage of needed and available nutrition. The moral to be drawn from these cases is that culture is a system of connected parts and that in order to introduce lasting and beneficial change, we must first understand the cultural system we intend to change.

Let us now turn to the discipline of anthropology and its subfields and methods. The three principal subdivisions, if you will permit an oversimplified statement, are physical anthropology, archaeology and ethnology. These fields are quite related to each other in terms of their joint aim of understanding man and his works, but they diverge in their methods and techniques.

The essential method in ethnology, which means the

study of culture, is that of going to live in the community whose culture the anthropologist wishes to learn and describe, whether this is in the wilds of Africa or the outskirts of Boston. The anthropologist prefers to remain in the community for a long time—not just days or weeks in the manner of a traveler or a junketing congressman, but many months or even years. He proceeds slowly, observing what he can and learning the language if this is new to him. He comes to know a number of local informants particularly well, conducting formal and informal interviews. Depending on the situation, he may make maps, give tests, take pictures. In any case he keeps daily and detailed records of his observations and interviews. His immediate purpose is to write an ethnographic report, a descriptive account of a particular culture—the ideal patterns as the people conceive them, the behavioral patterns as the observer finds them, the variations between subgroups.

The long-range purpose of the ethnologist is twofold. For one thing he seeks to reconstruct the growth and spread of the world's cultures. He wants to know, for example, how the native cultures of the New World arose in advance of the Europeans' arrival on the scene; he wants to trace the origins of writing; he wants to know countless other things about the history of culture. But in addition, he looks for "laws" or generalizations concerning the nature of culture and the dynamics of culture change. Both purposes, recovering history and discovering processes, depends on comparing various well-studied cultures or societies.

The physical anthropologist studies living man and fossil man, as well as the primates, both living and fossil. He studies physical behavior, human genetics, body growth and body types. He uses calipers, photographs, x-rays and a great array of other techniques developed to advance this specialized branch of anthropology. Like the ethnologist, the physical anthropologist is equally interested in history and process, but on the biological rather than the cultural level. He asks questions such as these: When and where did man diverge from the other primates? How did his present form evolve? What are the present races, how did they come into being, and what significance can we attach to racial differences? He is interested in the phenomenon of race mixture, how it occurs and what it shows. He is interested in exploring possible relationships between body build on the one hand and health and performance on the other. He is interested in the effect of environmental stress on the structure and function of the body.

The bearing of physical anthropology upon medicine is quite direct and fairly evident. Physical anthropologists hold appointments in anatomy departments in several of our medical schools. Because of their familiarity with minute anatomical differences in man, physical anthropologists are able to classify, catalogue and study different human populations; to sift, compare and distinguish recovered skeletal remains of vanished eras; and to serve as experts in cases of legal medicine. If there is need to assist the police by identifying human bones, they can often make shrewd estimates as to the age, sex and race of the individual at issue.

Studies of ancient human fossils and of contemporary primates such as the gorilla and chimpanzee enable students of physical anthropology to increase our scientific understanding of adaptive evolution, the process culminating in the present human form with its strengths and weaknesses deriving from the ancestry of man. The high incidence of low back trouble is partly traceable to the upright posture man assumed when he or his evolutionary precursors became stable on two legs. Apes too have low back trouble, but the incidence is much lower than in man.

Patterns of growth and maturation constitute a special field of inquiry on the part of physical anthropologists. In making these inquiries, they help to establish needed norms and standards against which physicians and other health practitioners can evaluate the status of children and patients. Physical anthropologists also study the genetic transmission of certain diseases and anomalies through family lives.

Archaeology, one of the three main subdivisions of anthropology, is the investigation of past cultures or cultural periods. This is done by carefully unearthing material remains: tools, tombs, pots and the like. An important aim of archaeology is to extend the history of man's civilization past the scant five thousand years since writing became part of our cultural heritage, to push back the curtain of ignorance toward the origin of man and culture hundreds of thousands of years ago. Among the contributions of archaeology to medicine is the unearthing of skeletons from which inferences can be made about the origins of surgery and about the antiquity and prevalence of diseases which leave their mark on the bony structure. A less evident but equally interesting contribution which archaeology conceivably can make is to give us a better time perspective. As archaeologists reconstruct and compare cultural successions and sequences, we get a little insight into the life cycles of civilizations—their birth, development and senescence. Comparing what happened in Egypt, in Mesopotamia, on the Indus River, in ancient China, in

Peru, and in Middle America, we can see the progression from food gathering to agriculture and eventually to cities and priesthoods and social stratification and the development of a military apparatus. From these comparisons we may yet derive some general principles about the growth pattern of cultures. With this perspective, gained from plunging back into prehistoric times, we may be able to gauge some day whether our own civilization is growing or aging, whether it is vigorous or weary, whether it needs medicine or surgery and whether either would do it any good.

My own particular specialty in the domain of anthropology is not in physical anthropology nor archaeology, but in ethnology or cultural anthropology. In the medical field particularly I am frequently asked, "why do you people go to far places, to Fiji and New Guinea and Uganda? We have exotic customs here in Boston and in New York that you people ought to study." It's a good question and I have three answers to give, having had some practice at it by now. First, anthropologists are interested in cultures wherever they are. It isn't their primary task to help Americans. They are not biased. They like a culture out in the Pacific as well as one on the east coast or on the west coast of America. Our own culture, prolific, big, important, and powerful as it is, is still only one of many cultures. Moreover, other disciplines, sister disciplines in the social sciences, like sociology, psychology and the rest, are so busy tilling the home field, that if the anthropologists don't study the cultures of the distant places, who will study these cultures which will not go on in their present form forever? Who will study this very important branch of human knowledge? That, then, is the first answer. There is a division of labor.

Benjamin D. Paul

Secondly, distance and difference provide a perspective that is hard to get by studying your own culture first. Just as some physical anthropologists gain perspective by seeing man in the range of the primates and other animals, just as archaeologists try to gain perspective by lengthening backwards the time span and increasing the series of cultural processes, so ethnologists try to gain perspective through space by comparing one extant culture with another and by studying one that diverges from the one in which the ethnologist is raised. This serves several purposes. It breaks the perceptive "set" as it were. He gets that fresh look by seeing something for the first time. You don't see the things about you because they're so much taken for granted. It has often been said that a fish would be the last one to discover water. And so, if you can leave water, you can come back and see that you have it.

In addition, because anthropologists frequently go to smaller scale cultures—smaller in terms of the number of people that comprise the society that bears that culture—they are somewhat more able to see the whole of culture instead of getting into one segment and seeing culture only in terms of economics or religion or political science.

By sudden contrasts, the anthropologist realizes how much of human behavior in his own society is not just given, not just natural or obvious, but is bound by the culture of his particular society. He goes to another where competition is a kind of a sin and he comes back and he says, "Well, competition may be fine in America, but it isn't inherent in mankind." Or, he may find that the bedside role of the doctor is something quite different elsewhere from what it is here, and realize for the first time that it just doesn't inhere in nature, it is part of culture. The patient has expectations and the doctor has certain expectations.

76

My third answer to the problem of why anthropologists don't turn to our own society is that some anthropologists, and these in increasing numbers, *are* turning to American society and are beginning to make studies within our own back yard. Anthropologists have a fine contribution to make in the international health field particularly. They can act as guides in the very difficult step of crossing the bridge between different cultures. This has been their bailiwick. There are anthropologists who are not only working in the international field, but specifically with health organizations. An anthropologist, now in Peru, is working with the World Health Organization; another, in Central America, works with a nutritional institute; others, in Brazil and elsewhere are working on health programs.

Anthropologists are beginning to bring to bear their perspective, gained through these outside studies, on problems of culture and medicine in America. Many promising fields are even now being exploited and still others await exploitation. One is the study of the hospital subculture. Just as anthropologists have gone into other cultures and participated, as it were, by living to some extent the life of the people, at least one anthropologist has had himself put into a hospital as a patient, and recorded what it is like to be a patient and see the hospital from the point of view both of an anthropologist and a patient. His view is quite different from that of the psychiatrist or nurse. Other anthropologists are working in different hospital settings, in Kansas, California, Boston and elsewhere. This is a rich and promising field with very practical implications for medical action.

A second area within the United States in which anthropologists are contributing is that of ethnic subcultures. Within the United States we have not quite melted down the various cultures of people who came from different parts of Europe. In Boston, for instance, several scholars are making a detailed study of various phases of the culture of four subcultural groups: the Italians, the Jews, the Irish and a residual category called Yankees or old Americans. They are studying these with respect to customs of family life and patterns of raising children, and particularly as to how these customs and patterns influence psychiatric problems. How does the factor of being attached to one of these groups affect the incidence and type of psychiatric illness when it occurs?

In New York, by a very useful coincidence, an anthropologist is similarly studying Italians, Jews, Irish and old Americans, especially with respect to their reaction to pain. Concerning this study, let me point out first of all, that there are great ranges of individual differences among all peoples—Jews, Italians and all other people. Let me also point out that these people are in a degree becoming Americanized and in some ways are indistinguishable from their present cultural background. What I say represents trends and doesn't refer to any particular individual. Despite the fact that Americans are all becoming Americanized, the process isn't quite as rapid as we might think it is or might like it to be.

Now consider the reactions of Jewish patients and Italian patients in hospital with respect to pain. Both Jewish and Italian patients tend to perceive pain—real physical pain—as something that is uncomfortable. But, while the Italian tends to perceive pain as an uncomfortable sensation right now, the Jew tends to perceive pain as shadowing or casting a shadow on his health and on his future. Both the Jewish patient and the Italian patient tend to complain freely. One, the Italian, wants primarily relief of pain and welcomes the pain-killing drug, the analgesic. The other, the Jewish patient, primarily wants relief from the anxiety about the source of the pain and the meaning and implication of the pain for the future in other areas of life. Each wants different things. Both want the doctor to do something, but the Italian tends to want the doctor to banish his misery *now* and when this is done, he feels happier. The Jew, if his pain were banished by an analgesic, might feel even more worried. He wonders whether it is habit-forming, whether it is good for his health, whether it hides a foreboding condition. In fact, Jewish patients have been known not to take pills that were given them for pain relief but to hide them under the pillow. Now, this slight difference between Italian and Jew relates to other things in their subculture, their various time orientations. One is more present-oriented, the other is more future-oriented. It also cuts into other aspects of their culture. The Jews and Italians behave differently from each other in being expressive about pain, depending upon where they are. In the home, the Jewish patient will often exploit his pain to manipulate his relatives through his symptoms. The Italian will do this less because he tends to be guided by a conception of masculinity and manliness. It is not manly to complain in the presence of a woman so he waits until he gets to the hospital, when the woman isn't there. Once in the hospital, he will have no compunction about complaining.

The Jewish and Italian patient tend to have different attitudes towards the doctor. The Italian tends to have more trust in the doctor, especially if the doctor reduces the pain. The Jewish patient is more skeptical about the doctor and wonders whether he is just treating the symptom and not the basic cause. He will tend to "shop around" and get "expert" opinion and check on the diagnosis with other specialists.

Jews and Italians are alike, however, in acting out their

pain and in being emotional in the face of pain. In this respect they are both different from old Americans who tend to inhibit the expression of emotion in general and, therefore, the demonstration of pain. What happens, then, when an old American doctor and a Jewish patient confront each other in the hospital? As a creature of his subculture, the Jewish patient evinces pain to gain sympathy and service. His culture has taught him that this is acceptable and that it works in his own home. The doctor, however, is a creature of his own subculture. Like all of us, he judges others by his own personal standards. By his Yankee standards, the Jewish patient is exaggerating his pain and "putting it on." Here we have, within our own culture, a sort of crosscultural situation in which subcultural groups having different kinds of values and attitudes confront each other with ensuing misunderstandings and misjudgments.

Anthropologists can contribute to the understanding, not just of the ethnic subdivisions of American society, but also of the social class subdivisions of American society. Not only are there different social classes, but these have different subcultures, different values, different ways of expressing themselves. These differences have very important implications for illness and for recovery. A study in California, for instance, disclosed that if one compared various people suffering similar kinds of disabling ailments in a hospital, it was the middle-class person, not the lower-class person, who tended to prolong his recovery and convalescence following illness. That is, chronic invalidism is apparently more characteristic of middle-class people than of people of another class. One could speculate at length as to the reason for this. Whatever the reason, however, there appear to be differences in the incidence, types of disease, attitudes toward doctors, treatment, and so forth between subclasses of the United States, differences which to some extent crosscut existing ethnic divisions.

Finally, I shall mention only briefly the luxurious subculture of the health professions themselves. What are the values, outlooks, trained capacities and trained incapacities of the professional, as a professional? In this area, the sociologists are doing good work. The anthropologists will do good work in this area, too.

In summary, anthropology can add a new dimension to medical thinking—adding cultural medicine to somatic medicine and psychological medicine. It can make us also a bit wiser about the nature of man— of man as an animal, but with a place and a history in the realm of living things; of man as creator and as creature of culture that gives him purpose and directs his life. Anthropology gives us a glimpse of the interrelatedness of things, the interplay between evolutionary process, environmental pressure and current human behavior, and the interplay between man's political, religious, economic and value systems and the other subsystems comprising the totality called culture. Anthropology can give us a glimpse of the push-and-pull between constant pressures to alter existing ways and equally constant pressures to conserve them. Anthropology helps us understand the deep differences between the outlook of different societies—those with insightful "witch doctors" and special attitudes towards cattle, and those with psychiatric hospitals and with running ice water. It helps us to understand the still deeper similarities of mankind, the fundamental needs which underly the variable cultural solutions devised to meet these needs.

WHERE LAW AND MEDICINE MEET

By David W. Peck, LL.D., D.J.S.

LAW AND MEDICINE are not akin, but they have, increasingly, much in common. Medicine is concerned with the functioning of man as a physical being; law is concerned with his relationships with other men and society. The connection between the physical being and the social being is obviously a close one. Behavior, which is of equal concern to the doctor and lawyer, certainly cuts across the fields of law and medicine, carving a wide area in which the action of the individual can be weighed, his accountability measured and society's treatment of him fashioned only by combining, focusing and harmonizing medical and legal views.

We shall now roam a bit over the fields in which law and medicine meet. We shall see many close contacts and intimate relationships. We should look ahead to where they might meet, for there are domains of the law which medicine hardly enters, in which the employment of medical services could be most useful, and which offer the most challenging opportunities for cooperation between the two professions for the social good.

An interesting place to begin our observations is at the

beginning of human life. Embryonic life is of major medical cognizance and concern. Until lately, however, the law hardly took notice of the existence of life before birth and its entry into the external world. It was not in existence in legal estimation. Hence, if an infant still in his mother's womb suffered an injury through the negligence of another, resulting in his being born into the world maimed or crippled, there was no right of action against the wrongdoer responsible for the condition and a blighted life. That was the law of New York State by judicial decision until two years ago. Then the law caught up with reality and justice.

What is interesting about the case for present purposes is how medical and legal arguments were arrayed together in the assault upon and defense of the old rule. On the one side it was argued medically that it was difficult to prove or disprove how certain injuries befell an unborn child, and legally that a foetus in utero has no existence of its own apart from its mother, that it was not a being in *esse*. On the other side it was argued, and the court was finally persuaded, that the medical facts were no more difficult to ascertain than the facts in many kinds of lawsuits and that not to recognize legal rights consistent with the actual existence of a viable foetus was to sacrifice fact to fiction and perpetrate injustice.

Recognition and regard for the medical facts and their importance to the decision were not denied or minimized by the dissenting justices. On the contrary, the connection between the law and medicine in the case was emphasized as the view was expressed that if unborn children were to be endowed with rights, this dictum should not be given by judicial decision on the facts in a single case, but rather should be the product of legislative action taken after hearings in which the legislature could be advised, with the aid of medical science and research, not only as to the stage of gestation at which a foetus is considered viable, but also as to the difficulty of tracing causation from prenatal injury to postnatal deformity.

The most common meeting-ground of lawyers and doctors is in the field of personal injury litigation and its offshoot, workmen's compensation. Indeed, the major part of the lawsuits throughout the country are cases of personal injuries arising out of accidents. Here the medical facts and incidents are intimately involved with the law. The legal remedy is largely dependent upon and supposedly responsive to the medical facts and indicated medical remedies.

The nature and extent of injuries, the resulting incapacity, the prognosis for recovery and the medical attention and expense required for healing are questions which are uppermost in many cases and determinative of the award to be made. Medical testimony thus looms large in the trials of personal injury cases and consideration of claims for workmen's compensation.

A man is run down by an automobile. He sues the owner and operator of the car. The first question which a court of law must resolve is who was at fault in causing the accident. Was it solely the negligence of the defendant which caused the accident, in which case the plaintiff is entitled to recover his damages; or was the plaintiff himself partly at fault, in which case he may not recover damages. There may be numerous subsidiary questions of fact which a judge or jury must determine in reaching a conclusion as to fault. For example: Was the traffic light red or green? How fast was the automobile going? Was it on the right side of the road? Was the injured party looking where he was going? Such questions and the determination of the responsibility for the accident and consequent liability are the first consideration of the judge and jury in a personal injury case.

If the decision is reached that the injured person is entitled to recover, then the question arises, how much? The "how much" may be as hotly contested and require as much trial time as the question of fault or liability, and at this point the courtroom is apt to become as much a battleground of doctors as of lawyers.

More often than not the lawsuit which is tried to completion rather than settled along the way is complicated with a serious dispute about the injuries. The medical facts are not readily ascertainable, or at least they are not beyond controversy. One doctor is prepared to make one diagnosis and prognosis while another doctor is prepared to make quite a different diagnosis and prognosis. Frequently you would not think that they were talking about the same case, the difference between them exceeding one of degree and becoming even one of the existence of any injury at all, such as a brain injury or even a skull fracture.

Head injuries have become a fruitful field of litigation, with the widest disparity in medical testimony, because the presence or absence or extent of injury cannot generally be observed or demonstrated and opinions can stretch with the imagination or interest of the one expressing them.

Neurological tests may reveal something, but whether the plaintiff has constant headaches, insomnia or personality change is so subjective and impossible of verification as to leave wide room not only for honest differences of opinion but for negation, exaggeration and falsification. The risk in choosing between the real and fanciful and

85

in awarding excessive or inadequate damages may be considerable. In such cases not only is the credibility and integrity of the plaintiff involved, but also the competency and honesty of the medical experts, as well as the scruples of the lawyers.

There has been a regrettable tendency on the part of some doctors to specialize in giving expert testimony in personal injury litigation and to become expert testifiers. The emphasis then may not be on objective or independent medical analysis but rather upon personality and patter to persuade the jury to a view which the doctor has been retained to expound. There has been an equally regrettable tendency on the part of leading medical authorities and practitioners to avoid the courtroom. The retention of medical experts on each side is necessary and desirable, and any doctor should be available, but it is unfortunate if the doctor becomes so aligned with the side which retains him as to share with the lawyer the role of "mouthpiece."

Judges have long been concerned with the spectacle of doctors expounding diametrically opposing views with respect to injuries and minimizing or exaggerating them as suits the interest of the side which has engaged them. Judges have observed trials stretch out inordinately in a battle between the experts, leaving a jury confused rather than enlightened by the testimony. The feeling grew and took hold among the judges of this city that if a panel of true and independent medical experts, men whose authority and integrity could not be questioned, were available at the call of the court in perplexing cases, much time could be saved and a truer verdict reached.

This opinion was expressed to representatives of the bar associations and medical associations, and resulted in the formulation and adoption of a program for making available to the court outstanding medical men who would serve on a panel of independent experts. The panel, comprising leaders in various branches of medicine, was selected jointly by The New York Academy of Medicine and the New York County Medical Society. It was of the essence in such a program that the doctors called as experts by the court be beholden to neither side, and it was necessary, therefore, to arrange for their compensation without requiring either side to make a payment. No funds were available for this purpose, but the Alfred P. Sloan Foundation and Ford Motor Company Fund generously agreed, as a public service, to underwrite the program as a pilot project for a trial period.

The panel has worked out very satisfactorily. Each side is still privileged to retain and call its own experts, but the court may refer a case to an appropriate member of the medical panel at some time in advance of trial and receive from him a report which is also delivered to counsel for both parties. The results generally have been that the cases have been disposed of in shorter time and on a sounder basis than would be possible if left to the battle of partisan experts as well as partisan lawyers.

Indeed, the cases are usually settled on the basis of the independent medical report without the necessity of calling the expert to testify or holding a trial at all. The independent medical panel is thus contributing measurably to speeding up the judicial process. And the judges have no doubt that a healthy by-product of the plan and of the availability of such a panel is that doctors and lawyers alike, on both sides of a case, are more careful and controlled in their judgments and claims.

In only a small percentage of the cases is there occasion

to call upon the medical panel. The panel is so useful and valuable, however, not only in the cases where actually employed but also in general influence, that it should be integrated into our judicial system and court budget. The relatively small cost of doing this would be more than made up by actual savings in court time and expense; and the returns in better justice would be great.

The development of the panel has been a fine example of cooperation between the professions in aid of the courts; and on behalf of the judges, I should like to thank Dr. Craig and the officers of the Academy, the officers of the County Medical Society, and the doctors who serve on the panel for their important contribution to the administration of justice.

In workmen's compensation cases the medical aspects are dominant and generally constitute the entire issue, for the underlying philosophy of workmen's compensation is that cases of injury to workingmen in the course of their employment should be taken out of disputation and litigation as to fault, and that prompt, certain and fixed compensation should be provided in accordance with the injury sustained. This still leaves ample room for dispute both as to the nature and extent of an injury and as to the causal connection between the injury and the work. While causal connection between an injury and the work of the injured person is a legal question, it is almost wholly determined by the evidence as to whether there is a medical connection between the work and the injury.

A good example of this and of the difficult problems which may arise is the "heart" case. When a milkman, for instance, who has been carrying fifty-pound cases of milk for many years without any ill effect, one day lifts a case and suffers a coronary occlusion, the question is whether this is an "accident" as the doctor views it and whether it is an "accident" as the lawyer views it. The testimony in countless records on this subject indicates that there is a sharp difference of opinion among physicians as to whether such a condition could have any accidental connection with the work.

The opinion expressed by one group of physicians is that ordinary activity, the work that a man usually does, has nothing to do with the incidence of an acute coronary attack, that experience shows that such attacks are quite as likely, or even more likely, to happen at rest; another group of physicians regularly testifies that, when the underlying physical conditions are right for it, even the ordinary work a man does involving physical effort helps to induce the attack and it is therefore an accident.

It is interesting to note the number of cases arising both in the courts and in workmen's compensation tendering the issue of whether cancer has been caused by an accident. We had two cases in my court within the past year where the plaintiff asserted, and was supported by medical testimony, that breast cancer was caused or aggravated by an accidents. One was the case of a woman who was thrown and bruised in an automobile collision. A pimple which was shortly thereafter discovered in the breast and grew into a serious cancer, requiring radical surgery, was attributed to the accident. In the other case a man suffered a fall and his claim and medical testimony were that an existing but dormant breast cancer was thereby activated and aggravated into a mortal condition. In both of these cases the court had to entertain the varying views expressed by the medical witnesses, and delve into the medical authorities and texts cited pro and con as to whether trauma could possibly cause cancer, and closely follow and apply the more or less accepted postulates for determining whether or not a cancer might be of traumatic origin or effect.

Recently the Supreme Court of this state in the Appellate Division of the Third Department had to consider the claim that a carcinoma of the lung was an accident connected with work, and this claim was at least supported by a medical opinion that there was a causal connection between the development of the carcinoma and the exposure of the worker to a draft coupled with a strain in opening a locker door a few months before.

Thus, in the area of workmen's compensation as well as in the area of private litigation there is difficulty in determining the medical facts as between differing medical views. Here again the experts for each side are apt to become partisan and it has been found desirable to create an independent medical panel of the Workmen's Compensation Board.

Undoubtedly the administration of workmen's compensation could be improved by a closer check on the medical findings. A more carefully selected, experienced and better paid medical staff of the Board itself could bring more objectivity and control into the decisions and awards. But there is one thing, totally lacking in the concept and administration of workmen's compensation, which is sorely needed—that is attention to the possibilities of rehabilitation.

We have learned in recent years of the enormous opportunities in rehabilitating the sick, injured and incapacitated to a useful, productive and rewarding life by training and fitting them for suitable work. This science or design for living has never been applied in a field to which it could well be adapted. We should not be content either as a human or economic matter to write off the casualties of everyday employment in terms of so many dollars paid for a lost limb or other injury which incapacitates one for the work to which he is accustomed. A broader, more individual and more social view should be taken with the end and effort in mind of salvaging the human value and realizing the potential which may remain for a useful life. This philosophy practically implemented should be introduced into the Workmen's Compensation Law and its administration.

Enough has been recounted to indicate the close connection between law and medicine where injuries are involved. Fairly satisfactory working bases have been established for assimilating the medical and legal incidents of such cases and putting both the law and medicine through a judicial process which is supposed to result in justice in each case. Our procedures can be improved, but the process is basically sound.

We move now into another field of the law where medical connections are not so well recognized and where any process for taking account of medical facts and factors which are fundamental is almost wholly lacking. Our busiest courts are concerned with family ruptures, juvenile delinquency and crime by youth. Here we endeavor by judicial inquiry and legal directives to handle cases with so many facets that they cannot be viewed by any mere judicial screening or settled by any court order. It is utterly unrealistic to consider these cases in any conventional courtroom frame.

Take the criminal courts, for example, as they function with respect to youthful offenders. It is the ordinary concept and function of a criminal court to determine guilt or innocence, and if the finding is one of guilt to impose an appropriate sentence. But as the Chief Justice of the Court of Special Sessions in New York City, Irving Ben Cooper, has said, the determination of guilt or innocence in most cases of youthful offenders is incidental to any really proper consideration of the case. Viewed either as an individual or social matter, the serious and pointed questions are what causes and conditions have involved the youthful offender in crime and what treatment will be remedial and rehabilitating.

In the courts which deal with youthful offenders, there is not presently available any medical aid, although every judge of these courts knows that youthful crime has its roots in physical and mental conditions and that medical service is necessary for both the diagnosis and treatment of the offender. As much might be said of the adult criminal, but at least in dealing with the young the opportunities and chances of redemption through adequate attention and constructive treatment are more promising. It is vital, if the court is to do anything but an inadequate routine job, for it to look behind the offense and ascertain the relevant circumstances inducing the behavior, and with like insight and understanding fashion the remedial measures. In both aspects general medical, psychoanalytic and psychiatric services are required.

As an example, let us take the case of a schoolboy who was brought before the court for assaulting his classmates and stealing from his teachers. His vicious propensities could not be curbed by any corrective measures at school and he was placed in the hands of the law for the well-known corrective measures of a penal institution. His guilt of the crimes with which he was charged was beyond question and could not have even given the court pause. But a wise and humane judge was interested in why this boy was given to such malicious conduct. His interest prompted an inquiry and it was ascertained that the boy stuttered badly and that his stuttering occasioned cutting comment from his schoolmates and was a source of exasperation to the teachers. The psychological reaction upon the boy led him to respond in his own misguided way. The judge in this case was convinced that the stuttering was at the root of the misconduct, and upon his personal plea a psychologist took the boy in charge, with the result that he is now leading his class at night school, while working during the day with a business concern from which he has already received his fourth promotion.

Every youthful offender and every juvenile delinquent should have a thorough physical and psychological examination by qualified experts. The causes behind the crime or delinquency should be ascertained by such examinations and investigations by a social caseworker. In the same way the remedial or corrective measures which are taken in the cases of youthful offenders and juvenile delinquents must be dictated largely by medical considerations and in many cases will involve medical supervision and psychotherapy.

We have not begun to give rudimentary recognition to the medical and psychological aspects of crime and delinquency or to employ the aid of doctors, psychologists and psychiatrists in fashioning a program of reformation which is corrective, useful and sound. I have no doubt that past concepts and practices in the tratment of youthful offenders and juvenile delinquents will have to be completely altered and that we must get away from even thinking in court terms or of attempting to handle these cases in the courtroom. The legal process should be revised in keeping with the determinative medical and social facts, and we should devise and set up an integrated program for handling these problems and cases through a proper coordination of the offices of doctor, lawyer and social caseworker.

Likewise, in dealing with family disputes, we must conform court processes and practices with the known realities of life. The cases which come before the Family and Children's Courts are usually cases of sick people. As Magistrate Kross (now Commissioner of Correction), a pioneer in modernizing the insight, outlook and work of the Magistrates' Court in family matters, has put it, "We are learning to evaluate crime in medical terms." She finds that most of the cases of family disputes and wayward minors stem from physical or psychological factors.

In this court there is token psychiatric aid, but it is so inadequate as to be almost insignificant. The court does, however, have an Alcoholic Clinic which is maintained by the joint support of city, state and private funds, and which on a limited scale is a model in incorporating general medical, psychiatric, psychological and social services.

Law progresses more slowly than medicine. Indeed the law is notable for slowness to change, and delay is commonly associated with the law. Nevertheless law moves forward in accordance with political, economic and social change, although the advances are not so spectacular as they are in medicine. We do not have in the law the laboratories and research facilities which the medical profession and allied sciences have created. There are inherent differences between the way law is practiced and develops and the way medicine is practiced and develops. We do not have similar opportunities for discovery or experimentation in the law, and revolutionary changes do not happen. Yet we can learn much from our brother profession and take some leaves from its book.

The concept and practice of preventive medicine, for

example, are established. Ideas as to preventive law are novel, but it is perfectly apparent that in such ideas and the opportunities for their development lie new frontiers of the law as exciting and promising as anything in medicine. It is doubtlessly not coincidental that those opportunities are related to medicine, and that the indicated action and advance on the legal frontiers require close cooperation between the two professions. Furthermore, the advance and realization of the potential are dependent upon the spark and support of the laity.

The adage of an ounce of prevention being worth a pound of cure is quite as true in the law as in medicine, only we have neither preached nor practiced it. We just don't happen to think in those terms in the law and our thinking requires reorientation to reality. In fact, we don't even think in terms of cure. We don't speak of crime and cure; we speak of crime and punishment.

The economics of this approach is not the principal consideration, but as we are always confronted and frequently stymied by obstacle of cost in advancing recommendations for reform, it is appropriate to meet the economic questions head on.

What is the cost of our present system of punishment which is single-minded in its approach to the problem of crime and criminals and takes little account of the possibilities of cure? The exact figure is not available, but I calculate on the basis of known information that it must cost $300,000,000 a year to maintain the penal institutions of the country. Fifteen hundred dollars a year per inmate is the individual cost. There is no return on this investment. It is a dead weight on society.

What is the cost of crime in the United States? That figure is incalculable. More incalculable still is the cost in wrecked or wretched lives, in broken homes, wayward minors, juvenile delinquents, youthful offenders and finally chronic criminals.

Compared with these costs, the cost of prevention and cure is insignificant. But it is the constructive cost which stands in the way of doing a constructive job. For lack of the aid of doctors, investigators, and counselors, the courts are prevented from getting at either the roots of or remedies for family breakups, delinquency and mushrooming crime, and are relegated to the frustrating routine of issuing support orders or divorce decrees, prison or reformatory sentences, or turning offenders loose in the hope that they will mend their ways. The services of a social caseworker, marriage counselor, psychiatrist or psychologist to help either the parties or the court are practically not available. There is indeed something apposite in the picture of justice as a blind goddess.

The little pioneering that has been done points the way to better court and social services. The Children's Division of the Domestic Relations Court now has clinic facilities to provide psychotherapy for 300 children. This is a small part of the 6,500 delinquent children who come before this court each year, most of whom John Warren Hill, the Presiding Justice, describes as emotionally disturbed and needing treatment. The clinic treatment, while the children can live at home and attend school, is felt to be more effective and known to be much more economical than institutionalization. Judge Hill is anxious not only to expand the facilities in the Children's Division but also to extend them to the Family Court.

Chief Judge Cooper of the Court of Special Sessions and Chief Judge John Murtagh of the Magistrates' Court are pressing for the establishment of adequate investigatory and probationary services in those courts, emphasizing that the cost of such service, including medical, psychological and psychiatric aid is only $150.00 a case a year, as against $1,500 a year for incarceration. With only one psychiatrist available as against 5,000 cases a year in the Home Term of the Magistrates' Court, Judge Kross resorted to group therapy and found it valuable.

From these slight but hopeful beginnings we can build. We can largely save the human and the economic toll of delinquency and crime, mend many a broken home, and retrieve for good citizenship a large percentage of the unfortunates who are now lost. This is not only possible but assured by applying to the law and institutions of the law the sound principles and practices of prevention and cure.

Here is the great and challenging opportunity for doctors and lawyers to meet in the designing, planning and administration of a basic program of social health. Many careers must be devoted and dedicated to this program. The doctors, the social caseworkers and the judges must be educated, trained and supplied—and paid. Good citizens, forward-looking citizens, must provide leadership at the government level lest we be stopped by the wail from the short-sighted conservators of a false economy. What we cannot afford is the price of our unconcern. Law, medicine and the laity meet at the threshold of the social order.

IS PSYCHIATRY A SCIENCE?

By Jules H. Masserman, M.D.

IN MY *Principles of Dynamic Psychiatry* (2) I stated that psychotherapy, like other arts and sciences, had passed through two of its stages of evolution—the "mystical" and the "taxonomic"—and was now entering its final "dynamic" phase. Since an infinity of statements, all true in some sense, can be made about any subject, this still left our knowledge of psychotherapy in a state of incompleteness measurable by the number infinity minus one. But what is more disconcerting is the fact that a dialectically antithetical statement can be made with equal validity: namely, that man has always been more or less keenly aware of his desires, capacities and limitations and has therefore in every age epitomized their dynamic interplay in his poetic fantasies, whether these took magico-religious or ostensibly scientific form.

Thus in every age and culture from the Euphrates to the Arctic, man has projected three categories of gods, representing his own triune nature. The first of these categories was comprised of gods of blind, subterranean passion and fury, called variously Seth, Sin,[1] Ahriman, Dionysos,

[1] The evil god of Babylon, worshiped every seventh day (Sin-day).

Siva, Loki or Beelzebub. To counteract these, men also devised various demigods who, at their personal cost, were more helpfully and rationally regulative of man's behavior here on earth: Amon, Zoroaster, Apollo, Mithra, Thor and their beneficent kind. Above all these, however, towered awesome beings who laid down harsh and incontrovertible edicts as to the conduct of the universe: Ra, Ahura Mazda, Zeus, Vishnu, Wotan or Yahweh—deities who must be obeyed because they could reward or punish without reason or appeal. And thus we had in man's most ancient personifications the prototypes of what Freud regarded as the forces that govern man, called, in what he recognized were neomythologic terms, the id, ego and superego of man's own psyche.[2]

Nor were our early ancestors far remiss in their empiric understanding of how to alleviate man's conflicts and anxieties. From the ancient temples of Egypt to modern religious shrines, havens of refuge were provided for the harassed, the weary and the fearful, and in these hospices nearly everything we now know was then also applied to help troubled men.

For instance, Greece and Rome had quasi-religious sanatoria dedicated to Asclepias the therapist, a demigod who was taught his art by the centaur Cheiron, himself equipped for the problems and burdens of medicine by being a tireless horse with the head of a man. Parenthetically, Asclepias and his daughter, Hygeia, were eventually slain by Zeus for serving (Gr. theraps=servant) mankind all too well. Be their (and our) fate as it may, the com-

---

[2] "It may perhaps seem to you as though our theories are a kind of mythology, and in the present case not even an agreeable one. But does not every science come in the end to a kind of mythology?" Freud, S.: *Collected Papers*, Vol. 5, p. 283.

Jules H. Masserman

posite course of therapy pursued in the Asclepiad sanatoria
would proceed about as follows:

First of all, the patient professed his adherence to the
Cult of the Temple and was received into its faith and
protection. Next, he was treated by regulation of his food
(dietetics), his ablutions (balneotherapy), and his exercise
(calisthenics), while at the same time his physical well-
being was improved by the proper application of moisture,
dryness, heat, cold or massage (physiotherapy) and by
administration of measured potions of sedative, nepenthic
and other drugs. In intractable cases, shocks to the head
from electric eels applied according to the technique of
Scribonius Largus and Pliny the Elder may have been
used, whereas trepanation and, possibly, cortical operations
were by then a familiar derivative of traditional Egyptian
surgery. With most patients, however, emphasis was placed
on group therapy through music, dramatics and guided
discussions, supplemented by individualized sessions in
which the patient, reclining on a couch as was the custom
of the well-to-do of the day,[3] hired a philosopher to hear
and help resolve his perplexities. The topics discussed
could well have been the vegetative (psychosomatic), animal (id), and rational (ego-superego) components of the
patient's conduct, Plato's ideas as to the hidden role of
Eros in his dreams, and how to reorient his daily life so
as to re-establish sanity (sanos=health) of mind and body.
All this occurred in what we moderns like to call the
"mystical" phase of psychotherapy.

Nor, in considering the taxonomic efforts in our field,

3 Cf. Socrates' free association therapy of the reclining Strepsiades in
Aristophanes' comedy *The Clouds*. Strepsiades did not want to pay his
creditors and planned to capture the moon so there could be no monthly
bills.

can we justifiably maintain our superciliousness about "old-fashioned systems of classification" in psychiatry. For instance, after all his research into the cerebral physiology of individual learning, Pavlov was forced to adopt a classification of temperaments almost identical with that of Hippocrates and Galen—a system based in turn on a concept of regulatory body humors much like our modern ideas of the role of hormones. For that matter, we are now beginning again to appreciate that nosologists like Kahlbaum, Mayer-Gross and Kraepelin were masterful clinical observers still capable of teaching important facts about human behavior to many of our starry-eyed youngsters impatient to plunge headlong—and without a lifebelt— into what they like to call "depth psychology." All in all, taxonomy is an essential phase in our organization of knowledge, and the term is not synonymous with sterility of thought and effort.

Finally, we may venture to admit that much of mysticism and unscientific empiricism remains operative in the theory and practice of modern psychiatry. On the basis of a few clinical observations, often superficially interpreted, we still starve, choke, electrocoagulate or slice up irreplaceable brain tissue with a crudity strikingly out of proportion even with our present limited knowledge of the finesse and complexity of cerebral functions. And when the final results of such procedures are undeniably adverse, we say *post hoc* that the patient must all along have belonged to some category of untreatable "mental disease."

Equally illogical, though perhaps less immediately harmful to our patients, is the seductive use of typically mythological thinking in lieu of more precise formulations and operational deductions. This is exemplified in attempts to explain fundamentals of human behavior on the basis of

101

highly selected parables such as those of Narcissus or Oedipus, without recognizing (a) that if the complex interrelationships among other inhabitants of these fables (such as the nymph, Echo and Narcissus' lover, Almeinas, or Laius, Jocasta, Chryssipus, et al. v. Oedipus) were analyzed, nearly every human relationship would also be epitomized; whereas (b) other, more ancient myths (such as the saga of Seth, Isis and Osiris or the legend of Gilgamesh, Engidu, Ishthar and Uta-Napishtim) are paradigms of filial loyalty, fraternal devotion and social sacrifice that are as culturally significant to the mores of Western man as are the Greek exemplifications of autistic self-seeking or murderous rivalry.

And so, too, in seminars supposedly devoted to the discussion of unconscious dynamics, we are sometimes treated to serious accounts of how in one case "the ego bribed the superego" while "really being in secret alliance with the id," whereas in another instance the "id masqueraded as the superego" and thus "gained an advantage in a bitter battle with the ego" in which it also succeeded in "splitting" the latter neatly in two—all this until a casual visitor might think he were really listening to a quasi-Homeric tale of three Fates plotting and fighting among themselves inside some poor mortal's skull for the control of his body.

As you may gather, I am not opposed to poetic license in expression, but perhaps even in our modern thinking the bright seductive spirit of mystery and fable still shines through the thin drab Mother Hubbard of science in which we pretend to clothe her.

RESEARCH AND DISCOVERY

Psychiatry, as an objective science of man's behavior, has existed scarcely three score years and ten, but must we admit that it has added as little to the lore of the ancients as to man's knowledge of man? The answer lies in the deeper meanings of the terms *re-search* and *dis-covery*. If these are sensed, we have indeed, in the last seventy years, partially re-examined man's conduct and uncovered anew some of its determinants. These questionings have occurred both in the laboratory and in the clinic, and each locale has been the scene of invaluable clarifications and reintegrations. We can survey only with the utmost brevity what some of these contributions have been.

ANIMAL STUDIES IN PSYCHOTHERAPY

There is one incontrovertible advantage to laboratory work: if one asks intelligent questions, the answers one gets from electrons, from chemical compounds and from animals, though bewilderingly more complex in that order, are nevertheless relatively operational and thereby less subject to obfuscation by the prejudiced observer. The problem is, then, to put the answers in their larger contexts —a task particularly difficult in the vast sciences of behavior. Let us review some of the data.

It was Shenger-Krestovnikova (4), one of Pavlov's students, who in 1913 first demonstrated that experimental neuroses can be induced in dogs by subjecting them to adaptational stresses beyond their integrative capacities (ego span), and it was Pavlov himself who advocated the use of bromides as the sole therapy for such states. As described in detail in my *Behavior and Neurosis* (1) this work was continued along orthodox Pavlovian lines by Gantt, and extended to pigs and sheep by Liddell. Beginning some twenty years ago in my own laboratory, my associates and I have been particularly interested in elaborating these studies and reintegrating them with psycho-analytic theory and clinical psychiatry (3).

Since our results have been reported in a series of papers and books over the years, I shall note here only that we were able to confirm as "biodynamic principles" various analytic postulates such as (a) the relationship of so-called instincts to physiologic needs, (b) the importance of individual experience in shaping later patterns of behavior, (c) the role of frustration in eliciting seekings for displaced or substitutive satisfactions, and finally (d) the etiologic importance of motivational conflicts in causing deviations of animal behavior analogous to anxiety states, phobias, compulsions, somatic dysfunctions, regressions and even hallucinatory and delusional aberrations in man.

Even more germane to our present interests, however, were the different methods we tried of alleviating these experimental neuroses once they were established. Of the many investigated, some eight were successful in varying degrees and in various combinations. In briefest summary, and with their clinical connotations mentioned only *pari passu*, they were these:[4]

Change of milieu—A neurotic animal given a prolonged rest (three to twelve months) in a favorable home environment nearly always showed a diminution in anxiety, tension, and in phobic-compulsive and regressive behavior. However, these neurotic patterns were prone to reappear when the animal was returned to the laboratory, even though it was not again subjected to a direct repetition of conflictual experiences. To draw a human analogy, a sol-

[4] This portion of the article, with modifications, is reproduced from a previous brief summary of the therapeutic significance of animal experiments (3).

dier with severe "combat neurosis" may appear "recovered" after a restful sojourn in a base hospital, but unless his unconscious attitudes are altered his reactions to latent anxiety recur cumulatively when he is returned to the locale of his adaptational conflicts.

Satiation of a conflictful need—If a neurotically self-starved animal which had refused food for two days was forcibly tube-fed so that its hunger was mitigated, its neurotic manifestations correspondingly decreased. Hippocrates is reported by Soranus (perhaps apocryphally) to have utilized a parallel method in human psychotherapy. Hippocrates, it seems, was once called into consultation to treat a strange convulsive malady which was keeping a recent bride virginal. Discerning, after a private interview, that she was torn between strong sexual desires neatly balanced by fears of injury, Hippocrates advised the husband "to light the torch of Hymen" with or without the patient's consent. The results of the therapy are not reported.

Forced solution—A hungry neurotic cat was prevented from escaping from the apparatus and instead was brought mechanically closer and closer to the feeder until its head was almost in contact with a profusion of delectable pellets. Under such circumstances some animals, despite their fears, suddenly lunged for the food; thereafter, they needed lesser degrees of mechanical "persuasion" until their feeding-inhibition disappeared altogether, carrying other neurotic generalizations with it. This method is a variation of the Hippocratic one mentioned above, but entails a greater degree of activity on the part of the patient. In some ways, the "therapy" is akin to pushing a boy afraid of water into a shallow pool. Depending upon his capacities for reintegrating his experiences (in analytic terms, his "ego strength"), he may find that there was, after all, no reason for fear—or he may go into a state of abject terror and thereafter hate not only the water, but pools, swimming, and all future therapists. Because of the latter eventuality, ruthless force is generally considered a dangerous method in dealing with neurotic anxieties.

Example of normal behavior—An inhibited, phobic animal paired for several weeks with one that responds normally to the experimental situation will show some diminution in its neurotic patterns, although never to the degree of complete "recovery." In like manner problem children do better when they have an opportunity to live with "normal" youngsters in an environment that favors "normality"—although more specific individual therapy is nearly always necessary to complete the "cure."

Re-education by a trusted mentor—As noted, a neurotic animal, perhaps by the very virtue of its regression to earlier patterns of relationship, becomes exceedingly dependent upon the experimenter for protection and care. If this trust is not violated the latter may then retrain the animal by gentle steps: first, to take food from his hand, next to accept food in the apparatus, then to open the box while the experimenter merely hovers protectively, and finally to work the switch and feed as formerly without further "support" from the therapist. During its "rehabilitation" the animal not only re-explores and resolves its motivational conflicts but also masters and dissipates the symbolic generalizations that spring from this nuclear "complex": i.e., its inhibitions, phobias, compulsions and other neurotic reactions. This, indeed, may be the paradigm for the basic processes in much clinical psychotherapy. The neurotic patient channelizes his needs for help toward a therapist upon whom he transfers his dependent and other relationships. The therapist then utilizes this "transference" with optimal patience and wisdom to guide and support the patient as the latter re-examines his conflictful desires and fears, recognizes his previous misinterpretations of reality and essays new ways of living until he is sufficiently successful and confident to proceed on his own. Whether this be called re-education, re-training, rehabilitation or psychoanalysis depends more on the context of the problem, the necessity for thoroughness in anamnestic review and symbolic analysis, and the skill and thoroughness in the utilization of the fantasied and actual interpersonal relationships involved than on any fundamental differences in the essential dynamics of the respective procedures.

Physio-pharmacologic methods—As has thus far been indicated, some of the vectorial processes of psychotherapy can be isolated in principle and demonstrated operationally in the laboratory. There remains, however, the fact that various physical methods such as the use of drugs, electroshock, etc., have also proved clinically useful in the treatment of certain behavior disorders. We can here give only the most cursory supplementary review of further experiments dealing with this subject.

Action of various drugs—Preliminary tests of the effects of various sedative and narcotic drugs on normal animals showed that, in general, such drugs disorganized complex behavior patterns while leaving relatively simple ones intact. Thus, in one series of experiments, an animal was taught in successive stages (1) to open a food box, (2) to respond to food signals, including signs reading FOOD or NO FOOD, (3) to operate the signal-switch, (4) to work two switches in a given order, and finally (5) to traverse a difficult maze to reach one of the switches. If the animal was then drugged with a small dose of barbital, morphine or alcohol, it would become incapable of solving the maze but would still work the food switches properly; with larger doses, it could "remember" how to work only one switch; with still larger doses, earlier stages of learning would also be disintegrated until finally it lost even the simple skill required to open the food box. Conversely, as the animal recovered from its intoxication, its learned responses were reconstituted in their original order. If now the animal was made neurotic by an adaptational conflict it developed a new set of highly intricate and elaborate reactions; i.e., various inhibitions, phobias, compulsions, somatic dysfunctions or even sensorial disturbances. These, too, proved relatively more vulnerable to disintegration by the sedative drugs than did the simpler, pre-neurotic behavior patterns, so that if a neurotic animal was given barbital or morphine its anxiety reactions and inhibitions were significantly relieved. In effect, instead of crouching tense and immobile in a far corner or showing panic at the feeding signals, it could respond to the latter by opening the box and eating (in a somewhat groggy but comparatively effective manner) as though, for the time being, its doubts and fears were forgotten.

Drug addiction—In one variant of these studies in which alcohol was used as the nepenthic drug, the animals which experienced relief from neurotic tensions while partly intoxicated were later given an opportunity to choose between alcoholic and non-alcoholic drinks. To our surprise (and, it must be confessed, covert delight) about half the neurotic animals in these experiments began to develop a quite unfeline preference for alcohol; moreover, in most cases the preference was sufficiently insistent and prolonged to warrant the term "addiction." In further proof of its neurotic basis, the induced dipsomania generally lasted until the animal's underlying neurosis was relieved by the dynamic methods of therapy described above. It seems redundant to discuss the human analogues to these experimental observations.

Tension-relieving effects—In still another series of experiments we observed that the administration of hypnotic drugs (including alcohol) so dulled the perceptive and mnemonic capacities of animals that they were, while thus inebriated, relatively immune to the neurosis-producing effects of traumatic experiences. In this connection it may be recalled that many a human being has been tempted, through subversive experience, to take a "bracer" before bearding the boss, getting married, flying a combat mission or facing an audience.

Effects of cerebral electroshock—In briefest summary, we found that when the ordinary 60-cycle current usually employed clinically was passed through the brain of the animal, the resultant shock acted like an intoxicant drug to disintegrate complex and recently acquired patterns of behavior, whether these were "normal" or "neurotic." Unlike most drugs, however, electroshock produced permanent impairment, however subtle, of subsequent behavioral efficiency, even though this could not be correlated with pathological changes in the brain detectable by present methods. Weaker or modified currents (i.e., the direct square-wave Leduc type) produced lesser degrees of deterioration in our animals, but also had less effect on their neurotic behavior. All in all, these experiments supported the growing conviction among psychiatrists that electroshock and other drastic therapies may be useful in certain relatively recent and acute psychoses, but that the cerebral damage they produce, however subtle, makes their indiscriminate use replete with temporarily hidden cost and potential danger.

Lobotomy, topectomy, thalamotomy, etc.—Obviously, any cerebral operation will (a) produce a transient general disorganization of response patterns which may be temporarily desirable, and (b) result in a more circumscribed hiatus in the patient's response capacities—both effects being of possible therapeutic import. Indeed, recent studies by a number of workers, especially Bard, Pribram, Rioch and their respective associates have revealed exciting new possibilities for altering basic patterns of behavior by specific cerebral lesions. Thus, section of the head of the caudate or above Area 13 in the posterior orbital gyrus may counteract otiosity and release spontaneity and responsive activity, although the latter may sometimes take the form of vicious rage. Conversely, lesions in the ventral thalamic-cingulate-hippocampal-amygdaloid circuits of the "visceral brain" may tame and quiet even dangerously aggressive behavior, though perhaps at the cost of peculiarly regressive patterns in which the animal tastes everything within reach yet fails to learn from adverse experience.

Some of these findings are being tested clinically by Scoville, Dax and Radley-Smith, Grantham and others in cerebral operations designed specifically for various forms of psychotic behavior, with currently promising results. Work in this field in our own laboratory has indicated that circumscribed lesions in the thalamus and in the amygdalae may disintegrate experimentally induced neurotic patterns and overbalance the corresponding organic loss in adaptive skills by a sufficiently wide margin so that, from the standpoint of survival and apparent contentment, the animal is undoubtedly benefited.

Concurrently, we have uncovered one qualification that may eventually outweigh this in basic significance: namely, *that the effects of apparently identical lesions in different animals may vary with the preceding experiences of each*— a circumstance that underlines once again the necessity for dealing with each organism, from the standpoint of both etiology and therapy, as a unique, dynamic entity. In effect, each person behaves differently from every other because (a) he was differently constituted at birth and (b) because he has had different experiences; ergo: (1) he will react uniquely to any given cerebral lesion, (2) he will then need rehabilitative therapy specially tailored to fit his frame and mode of action, hide his defects and best utilize his remaining capacities for optimal adaptation.

MAN'S PRINCIPAL DISTINCTION FROM OTHER ANIMALS: HIS UNIQUE DELUSIONS AND UR-DEFENSES

These, then, are the leads culled from comparative and experimental psychology, rich in their implications of future contributions to clinical theory and practice. However, we cannot leave the subject of psychotherapy without paying *quasi*-Galenic obeisance to a sacrosanct belief held by most of us, that, whereas the organs, physiology and

nervous systems of other animals are disconcertingly like
ours, we differ from them so essentially that studies of their
behavior are interestingly irrelevant to the problems of
psychiatry. I submit, then, that men *do* differ psychologically from animals, but that the differences consist mainly
(a) in the complexity and versatility with which human
beings elaborate both "normal" and "neurotic" behavior,
and (b) in their possession of several transcendent articles
of faith (or delusion) which animals, at least, never ver-
balize. These Ur-defenses of man are:

1. *The Ur-defense of personal invulnerability, power
and literal or vicarious immortality*, rooted in primary nar-
cissism and never surrendered.

2. *The Ur-defense of the perfect servant or system*, expressed consciously in the belief that one can impose order
and security on a universe of chaos and danger by the inter-
cession of omnipotent and omniscient Beings who can be
controlled by wheedling, bribery or command, much as
one once controlled one's parents; or by the invention of
transcendent, mutually exclusive scientific or philosophic
systems.

3. *The Ur-defense of "Faith in Humanity,"* derived
from the almost equally illogical presumption that because
one's mother at one time loved and cherished one, the rest
of mankind must be almost equally provident and indul-
gent. This expectation of survival through dependence,
when combined with ancillary erotic yearnings and experiences, determines many of our interpersonal relationships,
including those in psychotherapy.

These are, of course, but bare statements that, taken alone, may sound dogmatic, unconvincing and perhaps strangely disturbing to many. And yet reflection will reveal how many transference phenomena and verbal and other therapeutic maneuvers resonate with these mystic, irrational, but exquisitely human and, therefore, ubiquitous beliefs, and consequently how explosive is the result of any attempt to traduce or abolish them either in an individual or in a society. While it may be too cynical to propose outright that therapy consists in re-establishing these and other of man's essential delusions in proper working order, wise psychiatrists eventually learn—along with wise teachers and ministers—that truly to help a man, one must help him rebuild in his own universe of fact and fancy, and largely on his own terms, his own beliefs in himself, in his fellow-man and in his personally conceived God.

REFERENCES

1. Masserman, Jules H.: *Behavior and Neurosis*. Chicago: University of Chicago Press, 1943.
2. Masserman, Jules H.: *Principles of Dynamic Psychiatry*. Philadelphia: Saunders, 1946.
3. Masserman, Jules H.: Psychoanalysis and Biodynamics— And Integration. *Int. J. Psychoanal. Supplement*, 1953, pp. 13-42.
4. Pavlov, Ivan P.: *Lectures on Conditioned Reflexes and Psychiatry*. New York: International Publishers, 1928, p. 342.

THE RELATION OF
ELECTROCHEMISTRY
TO MEDICINE

By Theodore Shedlovsky, Ph.D.

MEDICINE has been defined in a broad sense as the science which is concerned with the fundamental understanding, maintenance and restoration of health. Electrochemistry is concerned with the electrical properties of substances and with the transformation of chemical energy into electrical energy and vice versa. The operations of electric batteries and electroplating are familiar examples of such transformations. Like all science, medicine and electrochemistry have two aspects, theoretical and applied. The one has to do with basic knowledge and with the understanding of nature, the other with the utilization of such knowledge and understanding for practical ends, with the engineering aspects of science. There is an important difference between so-called pure and applied science which is not always realized, and which I believe may be of some interest to the supporters of scientific research.

If we wish to build an unusually long suspension bridge, for example, we can ask a group of competent engineers whether, with the existing technological knowledge and with the economic resources available, this project is feasible. If it is, we can further ask about how long it will take and how much it will cost. The applied scientists, the engineers, can answer these questions and perhaps proceed with the construction of the bridge. They can schedule the work and on a given Wednesday afternoon, let us say, plan to accomplish a particular task.

If, on the other hand, we ask questions about pure or basic science, such as, "what is the fundamental nature of a certain baffling disease? Can a cure be found for it? How long will it take and how much will it cost?" obviously no clear answers can be given, because one cannot know that one will get a fruitful idea on a given Wednesday afternoon. This is not to say that experimental scientific work cannot be planned; it is, and it must be planned. Science, however pure, has its engineering aspect.

Thus, organization of applied science—engineering—is not only desirable but actually essential for its effective performance. But fundamental science, whose progress depends on man's imagination and on new ideas, is better served by organization *for* rather than *of* research, that is, by the creation of suitable research facilities in an environment favorable for intellectual pursuit, and by placing the emphasis of support on people rather than on projects.[1]

How is electrochemistry related to medicine? First, electrochemistry provides the scientific investigator with powerful laboratory methods and tools for the study of such medically important substances as hormones, viruses, enzymes, proteins. Secondly, living organisms and, in fact, all living cells, are complicated electrochemical systems capable of transforming chemical energy into electrical

[1] Dr. Thomas Rivers discussed this question in his George R. Siedenburg Memorial Lecture on "Concepts and Methods of Medical Research." *Frontiers in Medicine*, 1950.

work. With appropriate apparatus the neurophysiologist examines such electrical signals to learn what he can about the function of nerves. The clinician, armed with a substantial background of correlated, empirical knowledge observes electrical signals from the heart or from the brain and is thus aided in his diagnosis.

Moreover, the relationship between electrochemistry and medicine is found both in theory and in application. The difference between these has already been mentioned, but it must be emphasized that they cannot be kept in isolated compartments. Without progress in fundamental science there will be no science to apply, and without applied science the laboratory will cease to function.

Electricity was known to the Greeks. This was static or frictional electricity which resulted from rubbing two different materials together, such as amber and fur. Later, it was found that the electric charges thus produced could be stored in apparatuses which today we call electrostatic condensers and which some of you will recall as the Leyden jars of earlier days—glass bottles covered with metal foil on both sides. During the eighteenth century the Leyden jars were fashionable in the hands of "natural scientists" and of amateurs who were interested in, and perhaps amused by, the sparks which could be obtained by their discharge.

It was Benjamin Franklin, born in Boston, who with his legendary kite and key experiment showed that lightning is "atmospheric electricity." Besides being a great statesman and patriot, Franklin was one of the great scientists of the eighteenth century and certainly one of the greatest our country has produced.

During the American Revolution another Benjamin, Benjamin Thomson, who was born near Boston, in Woburn, Massachusetts, remained an ardent supporter of the British Crown and barely escaped with his skin from the port of Boston. An able, adventurous, and ambitious man with a colorful career, he contributed notably to science, became Count Rumford and played a major role in founding the Royal Institution in London with its renowned "Layity" lectures. The Royal Institution through Michael Faraday played a most important part in the history of electrochemistry.

In 1786 an Italian anatomist, surgeon and obstetrician, Luigi Galvani of Bologna, observed that severed frogs' legs twitched when touched by two metals externally in contact. In earlier experiments he investigated the effect of electrostatic and atmospheric electricity (during a storm) on the "prepared" frog, being familiar with Franklin's scientific work. Galvani's observations, which he attributed to animal electricity, mark the beginning of electrophysiology and of electrochemistry in biology. His works were published in 1791 (the year Faraday was born and a year after Franklin's death) and soon attracted the interest of another Italian, Alessandro Volta. Alessandro Volta, after whom the unit of electromotive force, the volt, is named, was born at Como, in Northern Italy, in 1745. He was a backward child and appeared to his parents to be an imbecile. But nonetheless, he eventually became a physicist and at the age of thirty-four was appointed Professor of Natural Philosophy (physics) at the University of Pavia. He occupied this position with great distinction for forty years. In 1800, two years after Galvani's death, Alessandro Volta wrote a memorandum to Sir Joseph Banks in England "On the Electricity Excited by the Mere Contact of Conducting Substances of Different Kinds." It was read before the Royal Society and published in the Philosophical Magazine within a few months. He wrote in part:

"After a long silence (for which I offer no apology), I have the pleasure of communicating to you, and through you to the Royal Society, some striking results I have obtained in my experiments on electricity excited by the mere contact of different kinds of metal. My apparatus, which will, no doubt, astonish you, is only the assembly of a number of good conductors of different kinds arranged in a certain manner. Thirty or more pieces of copper or silver, applied each to a piece of tin or zinc (which is much better), and as many stata of any good liquid conductor such as salt water, lye, etc. or pieces of pasteboard, skin, etc. soaked in such liquids are interposed between every pair of the different metals in alternate series and always in the same order. This instrument imitates the effects of the Leyden Jar and far surpasses its virtues as it has no need of being recharged by foreign electricity (Electrostatic). To this apparatus which is much more similar to the natural electric organ of the torpedo or electric eel than to the Leyden Jar, I would give the name of the 'Artificial Electric Organ.' "[2]

Volta's pile was the first battery, the first electrochemical apparatus. How did it work and what about Galvani's frogs? These questions became the center of a long controversy. Volta, the physicist, maintained that the electric current was due to the metal contacts. Sir Humphry Davy, the chemist who was the Director of the Royal Institution in London and who experimented with the pile and observed that the zinc became more and more corroded as the pile was used, believed that the electricity came from a chemical change. Galvani, the doctor and biologist, had been convinced that his frogs contained animal electricity.

[2] Quoted from Translation in "Galvani-Volta." Burndy Library, 1952.

It took many years of work and thought—about a century
—to discover that they were all partly right but that their
"unitarian" views were wrong. An account of this story
would take far too long to expound here. It would require
a treatise on Electrochemistry including discussions of the
laws of electrolysis discovered by Faraday, of the ion disso-
ciation theory of Arrhenius, of electrons discovered by
J. J. Thompson, of the chemical thermodynamics of Willard Gibbs, and of the electrochemical work of Helmholtz
and several other pioneers in this field.

But let us return to the relationship of electrochemistry
to medicine. Electrochemistry has provided powerful laboratory methods for the study of many biologically important substances. One of the most fruitful of these methods
has been electrophoresis, the electrical transport of ionic
substances. The important components of blood, of pro-
toplasm, of the substance of living cells in general, are
enormously large molecules, usually proteins. These are
complex and delicate molecules which cannot be melted,
distilled, or treated in the usual manner which chemists
use in the study of simpler substances. One of the mildest
treatments one can impose on a delicate molecule, such as
a protein, is to make it move. This can be done by passing
an electrical current through a solution containing such
molecules, if these are electrically charged. Proteins are
so charged—in fact, positively if the solution is more acid
and negatively if the solution is more alkaline than the
so-called isoelectric point, which is that pH value or acidity of the solution at which the particular protein in question has no net charge at all. If a solution of fixed acidity
(pH) and containing a mixture of proteins is stratified in a
tube below a similar solution but without these proteins
(the buffer), and an electric current is made to flow through

the tube, the originally present boundary of stratification will in general give rise after a time to several boundaries across the path of the current. This is because different proteins will generally move at different rates under the influence of the electric field, although this is not necessarily so. Two different proteins may happen to behave similarly in this respect, just as two chemical compounds may happen to possess some other particular property in common.

We have just described the principle of the moving boundary method of electrophoresis. It was first tried by Hardy in England in 1905, and in 1937 Tiselius in Sweden published his classic paper on "A New Apparatus for Electrophoretic Analysis of Colloid Mixtures" which resulted in the creation of a laboratory dimension for the investigation of biologically important substances. Because protein solutions are usually without color, special optical means are required for the observation and recording of the moving boundaries which reveal the electrical mobilities and relative quantities of protein components under study. Longsworth, in this country, added materially to this important development.

Thanks to electrophoresis, the proteins of blood serum have been resolved into the so-called alpha, beta, and gamma globulins in addition to albumin. We have learned that the gamma globulin group contains the various antibodies or immunity substances, such as will protect a child against measles, for example; the beta globulin group contains most of the fatty or lipo proteins; alpha globulin is usually increased in amount when there has been appreciable tissue destruction, whether it be from infection, fractures or other causes. But perhaps the greatest usefulness of electrophoresis in medicine has been the fact that it has provided means for effectively characterizing and fractionating substances of fundamental importance in understanding and influencing living matter.

Living matter or a living cell is not a mere assembly of chemical compounds, however. It is an oriented, dynamic system of complex materials in constant interaction with the environment, a complex chemical laboratory manufacturing many compounds no chemist has yet been able to make, by methods which are the current puzzling problems of modern biochemistry. Here, the electrochemist's galvanic (or voltaic) cells are useful in measuring and sometimes automatically maintaining constant the acidity (the pH) of solutions or the balance between oxidation and reduction (the oxidation-reduction potential). Much of physiology requires not only an understanding of electrochemistry but also leans heavily on its tools.

Between the inside and the outside of a living cell there exists an electrical potential usually of about a tenth of a volt. It is true of plant cells as well as cells of mammals, birds or fishes. This is called the "resting" potential. In the case of certain cells, like nerve and muscle, this potential may be quickly altered and restored again, giving rise to electrical "action currents" in response to various stimuli. The theory of the fundamental electrochemical mechanism underlying "resting" and "action" potentials is controversial. But most workers agree that the phenomena depend largely on differences in ionic mobilities across the so-called "electrical membrane" which is known to exist but about which practically nothing is known apart from its mode of action and the fact that it must be exceedingly thin. Let us not enter this controversy here since it is too technical and complex. Suffice it to say that real but slow progress is being made in understanding the fundamental problem.

121

Although we are not yet clear on just how the cell works as a bioelectrically functioning system, we can, nevertheless, make empirical correlations between the cells' electrical signals and clinical experience, and these have proven to be exceedingly useful.

The electrocardiograph (E.C.G.), familiar to us all, records the electrical activity of the heart during the spread of an activating impulse and its retreat over the auricular and ventricular structures. Since the early work of Ludwig and Waller (1887) and Einthoven's apparatus and ideas (1903) much data has been accumulated, so that today the E.C.G. is an invaluable aid to the clinician.

The electroencephalograph (E.E.G.) which measures and records the electrical activity of the brain, in a manner analogous to the E.C.G. for the heart, has not yet been as rewarding. Here the technique is newer and a bit more complicated. The apparatus is somewhat more elaborate. But with a greater backlog of data and experience there is no reason to suppose that in time it may not match the E.C.G. in practical importance. It has already shown its value in locating brain injuries, tumors, etc., and in experimental work with epilepsy and certain other conditions. It is interesting to note that thought and mood changes show no significant correlation with brain potentials, but that differences between sleep and wakefulness, or opening and closing of eyes can be readily detected.

If medicine is indebted to electrochemistry for practical aid, electrochemistry is indebted to biology for the problems it has raised. It may be appropriate to close with a quotation from a remarkably prophetic passage from a Florentine, Felice Fontana, who in 1781, before Galvani and Volta, wrote in a "Treatise on the Viper":

"We are not only ignorant of muscular motion, but we cannot even imagine any way to explain it, and we shall apparently be driven to have recourse to some other principle; that principle, if it be not common electricity, may be something like it and it may follow the most common laws of electricity. It may likewise be modified in nerves as in the torpedo. We must first assure ourselves by experiments whether there is really an electrical principle in contracting muscles; we must determine the laws that this fluid observes in the human body; and after all it will yet remain to be known what it is that excites this principle and how it is excited. How many things are left in an uncertain state to posterity!"

PSYCHIATRY—PAST AND PRESENT

By Clarence P. Oberndorf, M.D.

THE SPECIALTY of psychiatry is not really very old as specialties in medicine go. But long before psychiatry was gathered into an organized discipline, many of the ideas now incorporated in psychiatric theory and practice were well known to philosophers from Plato to Schopenhauer, to Montaigne, and our own Benjamin Franklin, to bridge very quickly an extremely wide chronological gap. Perhaps one of the very first textbooks in this country on psychiatry was that by Dr. Benjamin Rush, a signer of the Declaration of Independence, an outstanding citizen and physician of his time, and a contemporary of Benjamin Franklin.

In his physiological approach to mental disease, Rush followed the methods principally in vogue in his day—particularly bleeding—as even today psychiatrists treating mental disease with physiological means are apt to try the most favored contemporary drugs and procedures—just now cortisone, carbon dioxide, and shock not necessarily induced by insulin. But Rush also was fully cognizant and appreciative of the psychological influences in the production of mental disease and regarded many forms of mental aberration as the result of social influences. Modern, indeed, was Rush when he advocated special hospitals for the treatment of alcoholics, for he thought that alcoholism was a disease caused first and foremost by disturbances in the emotional life of the individual. In the matter of criminality, too, he observed that treatment rather than the ax or halter should be the procedure in many deviations which at that time were treated by capital punishment.

But psychiatry as a specialty outside of the custodial care of the insane made slow progress both in America and abroad. Indeed, generally speaking, throughout the nineteenth century the advances in psychiatric treatment were largely in the improved care of patients who had been committed to mental hospitals. In the most advanced of these hospitals, many of the so-called modern accessories, such as occupational therapy, dancing, music, and especially agriculture and horticulture, etc., were strongly advocated in this country as well as in Europe.

The wise general practitioner of the early days was an empiric psychiatrist, and usually such a psychiatrically intuitive medical man was the most successful in his community, for in many cases he usually treated emotionally motivated situations with encouragement, reassurance or advice topped off by some innocuous medication known as a placebo. With the concentration of treatment in hospitals, where the individuality of the patient is often lost and he becomes a "Cardiac in Bed 12," this type of personal contact has to a large extent disappeared. The same may be said in the case of the private patient whom the vanishing family physician quickly refers to various specialists, including the psychiatrist, for an opinion.

I am not entirely sure that the attempt to meet this by having a psychiatrist interview the patient who does not react in the customary way to his illness, the doctors, or his hospitalization, remedies this deficiency, although this in itself evidences a twentieth-century appreciation of the influence of mind over matter on the part of the physician in charge of the case. Often the psychiatrist makes an objective report of the patient's difficulties, sometimes couched in scientific terms, which ornaments the chart but which does not effectively influence the various specialists in meeting the patient's emotional needs. In recent years, in progressive hospitals an attempt has been made to remedy this deficiency by making the psychiatrist see the patient more often and thus becoming an active participant in the treatment.

Prior to 1900 the treatment of most functional psychiatric troubles—nervous breakdowns, as they were often euphemistically called—consisted in the rest cure of Weir Mitchell, neurologist and novelist, who devised a method whereby the neurotic patient remained in isolation for a period of from three to six weeks, removed from his usual contacts and fed ample quantities of nourishing foods. In favor, too, were a change of scene or environment, such as sending the patient on a trip, or if able to afford it, to one of the spas in Europe, administering drugs or sedatives, particularly bromides. Foul-tasting, actually punitive drugs, such as valerian or asafetida, were also used. These latter perhaps may have benefited the patient in that through submission to such punishment he may have mildly expiated some sense of guilt which was associated with his mental disorder.

Many of the prominent neurologists of that time owned private sanitaria where such treatments were carried out. They usually bore the physician's name, such as Dr. Johnson's or Dr. Jones' Sanitarium, identifying the institution with its head. In 1909, shortly after I joined the outpatient clinic in neurology at Cornell under the direction of Dr.

C. L. Dana, an eminent scholar and neurologist, I said to one of the older neurologists in the clinic that it was my hope, some day, also to have a sanatorium of my own. He was a bluff, tobacco-chewing Irishman, a veteran of years of service as physician in such institutions, but when he heard my remark he cried at me: "What has gotten into you, Obie? Why in Hell do you want to run a boarding house for a lot of loonies?"

I had never thought of the sanitarium in just that light, but suddenly the truth of this statement dawned upon me, and never since have I had any desire to be associated even indirectly through participating in the ownership of a sanitarium, much less actually to have my name attached to one. I regret to say that even today some of the private sanitaria still fall within the definition my blunt friend gave forty years ago, with the exception that nearly all of them have installed apparatus by which electric shock is administered—sometimes without due consideration for its indication.

On the other hand there exist today several private or semi-private sanitaria where the level of treatment is of the best and which have made valuable contributions to the study of psychiatric and social needs of hospitalized patients. Aided and supported by the mental hygiene movement and a liberalization of state hospitals, these private institutions also have done much in their own communities to remove the stigma formerly and to some extent still attached to the hospitalization of mental patients in public as well as private hospitals. The sanitaria which I now have in mind are geographically widely scattered over the country and show great skill in safeguarding the patient's interests where legal matters are concerned and in timing their discharge and aftercare, as well as enlightening and instructing the families on attitudes they should cultivate if they wish to assist in the return of the patient to the community and his continued residence there.

It so happened that when I entered Bellevue Hospital in 1906 as an intern on the medical division, there—as in other Metropolitan hospitals—the value of the psychological approach was recognized in cases called hysteria, neurasthenia, or psychasthenia, and was appreciated by certain attending physicians, though of course, not nearly to the extent that it is today since psychoanalytic thinking has influenced medical men, and "psychosomatic" has become a popular term. Also, at the beginning of the century a special psychopathic division had been established on the grounds of Bellevue to care for the acutely mentally ill. This service was in charge of Dr. Menas Gregory, whose intuitive perception in this specialty was second to none of the eminent psychiatrists whom I later met here and abroad.

The medical and other services of Bellevue did not hesitate to call into consultation the staff of the psychopathic ward in cases where the question arose as to whether the patient was suffering from a physically or psychologically induced morbid condition.

I should say that during the first decade of the century probably no more than a dozen physicians in private practice in New York City devoted themselves exclusively to the care of persons suffering from mental disorders. They were called brain specialists or alienists, the latter largely concerned with problems of medical jurisprudence. The neurologists, who were already numerous, included the care of mental illnesses in their diverse and often incongruous practice.

At about this time two great discoveries made their impact on the practice of psychiatry.

The first, of course, was the discovery of the Wassermann reaction for the diagnosis of cerebral spinal syphilis, and drugs which could arrest it. Syphilis was indeed widely prevalent in the community and no respecter of class or occupation. It would be quite impossible for the present generation of psychiatrists to picture the tremendous advance in diagnosis and therapy made through this discovery, for the great variety in the character of the initial symptoms in cases which eventually turned out to be paresis had caused tremendous difficulty in diagnosis. There was no way of determining whether the patient suffered from neurasthenia, depression, mania, or some other emotionally determined psychic disorder, or from mental deviation caused by the invasion by the spirochete of the cerebrospinal system.

The second great change in the treatment of mental disorders can be attributed overwhelmingly to a new method which Sigmund Freud had been developing during the last ten years of the previous century. Within the last three years we have learned, through the publication of letters from Freud to the Berlin laryngologist, Wilhelm Fliess, of the self-sacrifice and courage which were required of Freud to pursue dauntlessly his search for truth. Freud himself suffered from many complaints, such as cardiac disturbance, headaches, and even fainting attacks, concerning the nature of which great difference of opinion existed among the various doctors whom he consulted. He must vaguely have sensed the unconscious factors which caused those other neurotic symptoms, such as a fear of traveling, and he determined to investigate them. As a result, he evolved a method to which he gave the name of psychoanalysis. It may be worthwhile to note that when I went abroad in 1908 or 1909, to prepare myself to become a neurologist and psychiatrist by postgraduate training at the famed university clinics of Berlin and Munich, practically no mention was made of Freud's discoveries, although at the Swiss psychiatric clinic at Burghölzli in Zurich Eugen Bleuler and his associates had for several years been applying Freud's dynamic psychology to the understanding of psychotic patients.

In contrast to this general disregard in Europe for Freud's theories, at the advice of Dr. Gregory, I went for further psychiatric training to the Manhattan State Hospital as a resident. In the spring of 1909, I found the leaders of that institution thoroughly allied to psychoanalysis and convinced of the value of dynamic psychiatry. By this time, because of the Wassermann test, functional disorders could be separated from the paretics and chronic alcoholics with reasonable certainty. Those directing clinical psychiatry at Manhattan State Hospital insisted that the staff, in the study of all the so-called functional cases, should take into consideration the interplay of early emotional experiences with current manifestations. To be sure, although the effect of sexual experience upon the psychopathology of the patient was more openly accented than today, when the function of the ego and the role of aggression occupy more attention, the essentials of Freud's theory of the influence of the unconscious were understood and employed in the interpretation of symptoms, both in neurosis and psychosis.

This was the halcyon period of Ward's Island, where Adolf Meyer directed the psychiatric work until he was called to become Professor of Psychiatry at Johns Hopkins in 1910. He was succeeded by August Hoch who, as early as 1900, at McLean Hospital, Waverly, Massachusetts, was perhaps the first psychiatrist in America actively to use Freud's theories in the study of cases. It was also at this time that A. A. Brill, after working several years at the Central Islip State Hospital, returned to New York. He had spent some time in residency at the Burghölzli Hospital at Zurich, where Eugen Bleuler and his able assistants, Carl Jung, Karl Abraham, and others were busily and enthusiastically demonstrating the value of the Freudian approach in understanding the delusions and hallucinations and stereotypes of the mentally ill.

The ebullient Brill then began his private practice in New York as a psychoanalyst, the first so to designate himself in this country, although James J. Putnam in 1906 had already published an article on experiences in the study and treatment of hysteria at the Massachusetts General Hospital, with remarks on Freud's method of treatment by psychoanalysis. Brill, however, was the first to demonstrate in clinical practice the therapeutic advantages which psychoanalysis had over any previously practiced psychotherapy. Brill's intimate contact with Freud gave him a position of authority in matters of psychoanalysis, but Brill also had the courage to present his psychoanalytic theory in the face of obdurate opposition on the part of powerful leaders in New York and American neurology and psychiatry.

Nevertheless, because of the interest of men like Putnam, Professor of Neurology at Harvard, Frederick Peterson, Professor of Psychiatry at Columbia, and Hoch, Director of Clinical Psychiatry at Bloomingdale, now the Westchester Division of New York Hospital, when a young psychiatrist decided in 1910 to become a psychoanalyst it did not mean that he was "embarking upon a highly insecure career," as Alexander (1) says was the case in Germany as late as 1920.

Formal training in psychoanalysis at this period had not

even been proposed. For better or for worse, the early adherents to psychoanalysis and psychoanalytic psychiatry had to educate themselves as best they could by reading in German the works of members of the International Psychoanalytic Association formed at Salzburg in 1908, which included the contributions of Wilhelm Stekel, Alfred Adler, and Jung, who later went their separate ways.

As I have said before, persons with psychiatric difficulties, especially those not definitely psychotic, were usually under the care of neurologists, and were thrust into sanitaria or state hospitals. The same condition existed in the neurological clinics, for, prior to 1910, outpatient psychiatric clinics were practically unknown in this country. However, the chiefs of most neurological clinics did not care too much how the endless line of neurotically disturbed persons was treated; so Brill, Horace Frink, Morris Karpas and I in New York, and Isador Coriat in Boston— perhaps the first psychoanalytically informed members on the staffs of outpatient neurological clinics in this country —were allowed a more or less free hand in the methods we employed.

No one cared if we dismissed half a dozen "uninteresting" or "chronic" patients with a pat on the back, a brief exposure to the crackling sparks of the static electricity machine, and a prescription for triple bromides, devoting the time thus saved to the investigation of the dynamics of the illness of a single patient whose problems seemed to reflect Freudian theories. Quite often Frink and I used hypnosis in a crude combination with psychoanalytic principles, perhaps not very dissimilar from what today has been expanded and formalized into hypnoanalysis.

A third great and far-reaching change could be noted in the first decade of this century. A new concept of the responsibility and obligation in public health and social medicine took root in consonance with a new social conscience which was developed in the wake of the accumulation of huge private fortunes in the period of fantastic expansion which followed the Civil War. Possibly a delayed sense of guilt prodded over-rich tycoons to make amends for questionable methods through which they had acquired incredible wealth. Social work and social workers began to make themselves felt as a force, and physicians in general practice no longer thought that their function in the care of the sick had ended when, for example, a patient suffering from pneumonia regained sufficient strength to leave the hospital. It became part of his duty as a physician to see to it that exposure to hunger and cold did not bring about a quick relapse.

The same vicious circle was particularly apparent in the case of alcoholics and patients paroled from state mental hospitals. For the latter cases, especially, social workers were being employed to assist discharged patients in adapting themselves to home conditions. The socioeconomic factors in this group of patients as well as in many other groups were no longer evaded by the physician. So, psychoanalysis reached America at a time when this extended sense of responsibility in the social aspects of public welfare was beginning to be accepted by physicians and hospitals.

The comparatively easy acceptance of the dynamic psychiatry of Freud by American psychiatrists depended, then, not only upon the relative academic liberality of American universities as compared with the European, but on the fact that the interrelationship of mental and physical health was beginning to be widely recognized. While, of course, psychoanalytic principles encountered very strong

133

and bitter opposition from many physicians, particularly neurologists and numerous psychiatrists, as well as from the clergy and laymen, the psychological approach to the problems of nervous disorder was not too far removed from the psychic factors so apparent in the interaction of poverty and disease, crime, delinquency, etc.

In March of 1913, I organized at Mount Sinai what appears to have been the first outpatient psychiatric clinic connected with a general hospital (3). Although doubts were expressed about the feasibility of such a clinic because mental patients might molest visitors to other departments, it was soon evident that no such disturbances occurred. The prevalent stigma attached to mental disease was clearly diminished by the fact that these patients passed the general admitting clerk on the same basis as those suffering from bronchitis or varicose veins. Before long, physicians in other clinics began to transfer troublesome neurotic patients to this clinic and, by 1935, the single clinic with one doctor had become two clinics, each operating three days a week with possibly thirty physicians and psychiatric social workers, including occupational and recreational therapists. During the next decade similar separate outpatient psychiatric clinics were established at other general hospitals in New York and in other cities. These sometimes included the care of acute psychotic patients. In a number of general hospitals, including Mount Sinai, psychiatric inpatient services have now been initiated which usually focus their attention on psychic factors in illnesses such as gastric ulcer, colitis, asthma, arthritis, certain skin diseases, hypertension, and the like.

The psychoanalytic approach, more than any other factor within my memory, tended to erase the line which is supposed to divide normal conduct from abnormal. In the first thirty years of this century, many psychoanalysts in the United States as well as abroad felt that they were fighting for the establishment of a science and art built upon truths which were unpleasant and highly unacceptable to the consciousness of the individual and society at large. They regarded themselves as a little band of rebellious pioneers heroically attempting to establish a method which might eventually prevent mental disease and even reveal the secret of the soul itself.

The disastrous effects of mental illness among the soldiers of the first World War, so-called shell-shocked cases, as well as those who showed symptoms similar to shell-shock even before leaving America for the battlefront, led to an enormously increased interest in the nature of neurotic conditions which the emergency had brought to the surface. Many young physicians returning from Army service where mental disorders so frequently and drastically disrupted military efficiency, saw in the field of psychiatry an opportunity for public service; and psychoanalysis, at least in this country, was sufficiently well known to attract a goodly number to study its theory and therapeutic possibilities.

The era of descriptive psychiatry gradually yielded to the impact of psychoanalytic dynamics not only in the case of adults but also of children. Child psychiatry, a relatively new specialty, was nourished by psychoanalysis because of the importance attached to early impressions in the later development of abnormal symptoms and character traits. It began to flourish in hospital clinics and in schools for so-called normal children as well as in institutions caring for deviants, so-called delinquent, and mentally retarded children. This tendency in turn soon began to affect the teachings of leaders in the field of pedagogy, the sociological sciences, and gradually invaded theological seminaries of many faiths. As I have pointed out elsewhere (4), John

Dewey's theory of education, that learning is a process of individual experimentation to be used and explored by learners, both children and adults who participate in it, and that the basis for learning in a child should allow a maximum freedom of initiative rather than the absorption of facts from books and teachers, fitted in well with the emphasis placed by Freud on the importance of emotional experience in early childhood.

Public acquaintance with psychoanalysis had grown to sufficient proportions in 1925 to warrant the publication of a full page of cartoons, "Have You Been Psyched?" by W. E. Hill in the rotogravure section of the *Chicago Tribune*. Formal training in psychoanalysis developed in the East about 1925 under the direction of psychoanalytic societies which controlled their own institutes. The members of such societies feared, perhaps rightly, that if such instruction were entrusted to medical schools, the essential principles, perhaps the orthodoxy, of psychoanalysis might be undermined. Today the institutes or societies which are members of the American Psychoanalytic Association must conform with the high standards set by that organization. Interestingly enough, in this country at least, psychoanalysis has invaded formal psychiatry to the extent that a large number of young psychiatrists seek analytic training.

In recent years, a considerable proportion of psychoanalysts have begun to rebel against rigid therapeutic technique and dogmatic adherence to Freud's theories. They favor a flexible application of Freudian principles to fit the individual's situation, personality and current problems. Progress and experience in psychoanalytic teaching have brought out the need to avoid the microscopic examination of individual symptoms and to correlate them instead with the over-all picture of the mental disorder as a whole and its setting in the patient's environment and period of life. A strong feeling arose that the young psycho-analytic psychiatrist should learn not only how a predomi-nating symptom might be interpreted, but how to estimate its position and value in regard to the patient's mental disorder in general. Many of the conservative (orthodox) Freudians have been influenced by this thinking and have modified their technique to some degree.

The enlargement of the scope of conditions or disturb-ances where one tries to apply psychoanalytic treatment —character neurosis, borderline cases, and even mild psy-choses—has helped greatly in encouraging flexibility in therapeutic aims and methods. One may add in this con-nection the increasing popularity of group therapy which also involves change in aims and methodology in treat-ment. I consider this movement a distinct innovation in the utilization of psychoanalytic principles in the hope that it may benefit a greater variety of cases and a greater num-ber of people. However, its influence, other than suppor-tive, is extremely difficult to establish.

Like many other psychoanalysts who have had long clinical experience with patients of all age groups in hos-pital and private practice, I came to realize that the thorough acquisition of any particular method of psycho-therapy, even prolonged instruction in psychoanalysis, must be accompanied by skill and wisdom in application, and that no two cases should be squeezed in the same format. However, certain constant factors influence the psychotherapeutic success in each particular case. They are: (1) the nature of the difficulty; (2) the method employed; (3) who undertakes to perform the therapy (the personality of the therapist); (4) the susceptibility of the patient to change; (5) the time and even place when treatment is begun.

This view is less extreme than the conclusion reached by

Theresa Benedek, an outstanding member of the Chicago Institute for Psychoanalysis, who for more than twenty-five years has been one of the most respected practitioners and teachers of psychoanalysis. In a paper presented before the Chicago Psychoanalytic Society on March 22, 1949, but published only in November 1953 (2), Dr. Benedek said: "Psychoanalytic procedure is the unfolding of an interpersonal relationship in which transference and countertransference are utilized to achieve the therapeutic aim. The definition indicates that the therapist's personality (his emotional maturity, psychosexual stability and personal integrity) is the most important agent of the therapeutic process."

Some twenty-five years ago I was startled and chagrined when the brother of a patient, whose analysis occurred at the age of fifty-six and with whom I had had an outstanding therapeutic success, came to visit me for his own psychosexual difficulties. He entered the room with these words: "Doctor, John said I should come to see you. He says psychoanalysis is the bunk but you're a good doctor." But of course John did not appreciate that without the knowledge and my conviction of the truth of Freud's discoveries I would not have been able to employ them selectively to his benefit and to have been, as he said, "a good doctor."

While—as may be expected from a psychiatrist who became convinced of the enormous value of the Freudian approach nearly forty-five years ago—my remarks about psychiatry, past and present, have been perhaps disproportionately devoted to the psychoanalytic aspects of psychiatry, certainly the more recent picture would not be complete without some reference to the physiological and surgical attacks on mental disorder which have been introduced within the past twenty years.

I refer to shock therapy which began with a physiologic agent, insulin, and surgery, whether this be topectomy or lobotomy. Here we find that those who use physiologic therapeutic procedures often insist that they be followed by psychotherapy based upon psychoanalytic knowledge. Occasionally one gets a similar expression of opinion for the handling of a patient after psychosurgery. However, it is admitted that after psychosurgery the patient's will to get well seems to be weakened and that psychosurgery is most valuable in those persons whose mental disorder is of such intractable or violent nature that they are already lost as contributing members to society. After psychosurgery such patients are no longer uncooperative but become relatively tractable, amenable, and therefore far easier to care for.

While the important contributions which psychoanalysis has rendered in making more intelligible the problems of human behavior in corollary fields, such as anthropology, sociology, political science, in events of the past which have now become history, and in literary and dramatic productions, should not be underestimated, nevertheless what concerns the average layman is the value of psychiatry, and especially psychoanalytic psychiatry, in the prevention and cure of mental disease. An overwhelming majority of students in training at psychoanalytic institutes, whether they be under the aegis of the large and exacting American Psychoanalytic Association or others, are doctors of medicine who will use their prolonged and extensive postgraduate training to restore persons suffering from neuroses, depressions, psychosomatic illness and the like to happier functioning. To this group of medically trained therapists have been added a goodly number of individuals holding doctorate degrees in psychology, anthropology, social sciences and pedagogy, to say nothing of persons without formal postgraduate academic training who have become psychotherapists despite the strong opposition of the medical profession, with which I concur. I believe that the interest of the patient in this extremely intimate situation between patient and therapist which exists in psychotherapy is best safeguarded if the therapist is fully acquainted with both the physical and psychological aspects of illness and their interrelationship.

The title of this paper—"Psychiatry—Past and Present" —is sufficiently sweeping so that it would appear imprudent for me to venture a word about the future of psychiatry. But psychiatry, not more than thirty years ago called the "Cinderella" of medicine, and its younger sister— psychoanalysis—today, thanks to such movies as *The Snake Pit* and *Lady in the Dark*, have become highly popularized from Broadway to the Main Streets of small towns.

As I have already mentioned, psychiatry which at first scorned its younger sister, psychoanalysis, today looks to it for the solution of problems which strain psychiatry's resources—that is, the mystery of the widely prevalent condition to which we have given the name of schizophrenia, the equally baffling periodic manifestations of the emotional swing called manic-depressive insanity, the varying susceptibility of two individuals to the same trauma and the interrelationship of certain somatic disorders to personality types.

So, in some psychoanalytic institutes and psychiatric services of general hospitals, numerous research projects have been initiated to investigate these enigmas. Possibly the solutions will come not from psychoanalysis alone but by combination of the investigations of psychiatrists with those of biochemists, physiologists, biologists, and maybe the recently developed branch of nuclear physicists.

One cannot dismiss the discussion of psychiatry—past,

present or immediate future—without commenting upon the lack of sufficient facilities for the care of hospital and ambulatory psychiatric patients and the need for extensive preventive activity in mental hygiene. It is a fact that only a very small percentage of the indigent receive even perfunctory treatment. This is due in part to the insufficiency of adequately trained psychiatrists and to the great amount of time which the physician must spend with psychiatric patients in contrast to that required in most other fields of medicine. Whether this deficiency will be met by state or private funds in the future one cannot predict.

There is no doubt in my mind that the aid given by extramural psychiatrists in incipient and even severe psychic states has prevented a great number of people from entering closed mental hospitals. Nevertheless the population of these institutions seems to be constantly increasing and huge new buildings are immediately filled by patients who cannot meet the difficulties of life in the community. Possibly we may look to new methods of education and social values for the prevention of mental disease. At the present time endeavor in this direction, groping as it may be, seems to offer our greatest hope that illness devastating to patient and society alike may in the not too distant future be checked.

REFERENCES

1. Alexander, Franz and Ross, Helen: *Twenty Years of Psychoanalysis.* New York: W. W. Norton & Co., 1953, p. 14.
2. Benedek, Therese: Dynamics of the Countertransference. *Bull. Menninger Clin., 17*:201-208, 1953.
3. Oberndorf, C. P.: Psychiatry in a General Hospital, *N. Y. State J. Med., 43,* No. 15, August 1943.
4. Oberndorf, C. P.: *A History of Psychoanalysis in America.* New York: Grune & Stratton, 1953, p. 232.

LIFE IS FOR LIVING

By D. Ewen Cameron, M.D., F.R.C.P. (C.)

THIS TITLE—"Life is for Living"—is an assertion which intimately echoes the tones and speaks the words of which the mid-century has taken resolute possession. It is a saying worn as a badge by an increasing number of citizens of this period, a saying which denotes the determination and the direction of our deeds.

Others who came before us saw life differently. Some have seen life as work, and, to this day, this is how many of their descendants still see it. For them, all preparation for living, all that is learned at school, all that one hears at home, is shaped to that end: that they may live to work. In work they find their security. For them, accomplishment is not, as it is for more modern man, an expression of the pleasure which he takes in his own powers. They do not delight as a strong man to run a race. Accomplishment, for them, is justification; hence their anxiety demands endlessly repeated accomplishment, a feverish preoccupation broken by empty periods which are dreaded and avoided and must be filled by any occupation, no matter how trivial. Hence the tiresome turning of play into work: the organizing; that dreadful word, "recreation"; the invasion of the home by the wire recorder; the hanging of notepads on the walls of those rooms in the home where you might think that men and women would find themselves most securely seated in biological kinship with the immemorial customs of their ancient species.

Others, again, have seen life quite differently. They have seen it as a period of trial, of probation, a testing process, a place where we struggle with good and evil, attaining thereby our ultimate rewards. Life, for them, has been the acquiring of virtue. But we must say that no general agreement has ever been reached upon what precisely is meant by virtue. Very clearly, there is to be a restatement, within our times, as to the nature of man. Equally clearly, this cannot be based upon the private and peculiar views of some sect holding itself precious in its very particularity. It must arise from humanity in general; it must be written against the massive background of the ongoing forging of a world society, the ordering of which demands ideals and aspirations and premises which can be held in common by all mankind.

Down the centuries, and around the world today, we may discover agreement on a few virtues: kindness (at least to one's nearest dependents, but carefully excluding classes often large enough to include all the rest of humanity—classes of those who, we feel, do not deserve kindness); courage (always excepting, of course, the blind fanaticism to which, unfortunately, it seems it is our enemies who are the most inclined).

As soon as we leave behind these few common ideals, we pass into the realm of the purely local virtues, peculiar to some particular way of life and which, therefore, serve to separate in bitterness the family of man: the virtue of strict adherence to some special dietary customs, the observation of some peculiar ceremonies at the time of the new moon, the new harvest, the new year or the new baby.

143

For some societies, more active in the search for virtue than ours, life may be all but immobilized by ceremonies, rituals and taboos. One is reminded of Abner Dean's cartoon entitled, "The Accumulation of Virtue." He shows a figure (by the hair ribbon, presumably feminine) precariously perched on top of a high and all but toppling tower, a figure totally wrapped up, save for head, hands and one foot, in an enormous ball of intertangling twine.

The wide and anxious pondering, the longing and reaching out for a fuller understanding of our nature so that we may better prepare ourselves to live in the new world which we are building, wells up from two great sources: first, from our rapidly expanding knowledge of human behavior, and second, from anxious apprehension of the vastness of the powers which we have forged for ourselves —powers capable of at once transforming our times, or, if taken over by dark and twisted forces within us, equally capable of the most massive destruction.

Let us look back along the path which has brought us to this pivotal point in the historic process. We see in the earlier part of the nineteenth century, the extraordinary and unique flowering of the intellectual activity which we call science, and its most fortunate wedding to industry. Coming from this there has been an enormous increase in things and in power. We are long accustomed to the old wisdom, "knowledge is power." We have not yet tested the Einstein-like reversal of that statement, that knowledge and power are interchangeable. And yet they are, for the vast powers which we gain as individuals and communities have infinitely increased our capacity to gain knowledge.

Through the means of transportation and communication which we now possess, we can far more rapidly assemble knowledge than previously; and through our vastly developed administrative techniques we can coordinate the work of hundreds and thousands of individuals, can ransack the accumulated wisdom of thousands more from scores of different countries and from a hundred different decades, bringing it to bear upon the solution of a major problem, as was done in the case of the development of atomic power.

From this great accumulation of things, above all, has come leisure. Leisure was formerly the right of only a few; only relatively few of the many, many bright brains were free, in earlier centuries, to speculate upon important questions. All but this tiny fraction had to bow their heads continually to the instant necessity of earning enough to eat, of finding enough shelter to protect themselves and their families. And, still more certainly, they were bound and curbed by the continuous anxiety and insecurity of life, by the endless necessity of remaining in the lockstep-like society of the Middle Ages—because, in a time of scarcity, such a society was essential. You could not afford to be different; you could not afford to rock the boat.

Now, if we fit ourselves to live in this tremendous century, the possibility exists that more and more of us can be different, more and more of us can be allowed to explore different ways of thinking about things, different ways of dealing with things.

From the knowledge being accumulated by the growing social sciences, their laboratories and research centers, and from the thinking of an ever-increasing number of men and women, there is emerging a conviction that the clearest and most fundamental statement concerning the nature of man is embodied in the assertion that life is for living. This statement carries with it great and far-reaching consequences. The first is that life is its own justification, that we may reasonably find pleasure and satisfaction in the development and the use of our powers as individuals and, together with our neighbors, pass on to the further cultivation of what we have built. The second is that we can trust human nature. This can be said despite all the horrors of the two world wars and the disruption of a cold war.

The human species has shown a most remarkable capacity to survive and to expand its control over every living thing and over its material world. It would be strange, indeed, if it could not ultimately control its last remaining threat, namely, its own nature. But many of the old premises which still dominate us are based on the belief that human nature cannot be trusted, that it must be moulded into a corseted caricature, especially in those vital areas of sex and of aggression. There is a prevailing fear among many people of what would happen if they let themselves go, of what they might do if there were no policeman around the corner. There is a particularly intense fear—mostly among those who never have deviated from the path of extreme abstention—that if they were ever to cut loose there would be no stopping them, that they would sink into the most extraordinary debaucheries of a kind that, one must feel, only a starved mind could dream up.

But it is well known to those people who have had more confidence in themselves and in their own impulses, that to put one's foot upon the primrose path is not necessarily to walk to the end of it; and that, indeed, after a short time the primroses disappear and the path becomes boring.

A third implication which follows from the one we have just looked at is that we can be responsible for ourselves and yet not be overwhelmed by that sense of responsibility. At the present time, such are our cultural beliefs and such is our earlier indoctrination that only a few of us are able to become really independent.

For most of us, our basis of reassurance must, at least in some measure, lie outside ourselves. Some of us are confident mainly because of our families, some, because we are doctors—not because we are men, or a particular man. Others find their basis of reassurance in the fact that they are Americans or Spaniards; still others require constant achievement and are anxiety-ridden without such outside support.

As children, it is true that we need constant support. The world is too much for us, too large, too difficult. We must have the support of our parents' interest and understanding and affection—and if we do not have it, we are damaged. Later, we have to have the approval of our neighborhood and of our school group. But for some persons it is then possible to go on to find that basis of approval or security inside themselves. It is true that one may well listen to one's friends and be somewhat concerned if they do not approve. But the lives of all those who have shown great leadership in this long journey of man are records of how these outstanding individuals pressed forward to their great goals, often despite the disapproval of their friends or of their families. They felt that they had to go about their business even though, with sad regret, they had to part company with all those they had cared for and who had cared for them. Theirs is a maturity which is not yet general.

If we are to be responsible for ourselves, we must also accept responsibility for our social institutions. We must be prepared to see that they are ours, that we built them, we made them, and can remake them the better to serve our ends and those of our neighbors.

A last implication of this statement of the nature of man and of his life that I would like to put before you is that we should hold ourselves as being worthy of our own respect and our own affection. Deep within our culture is embedded the belief that man must first love his neighbors and, indeed, love them better than himself. It is true that, under special circumstances, our societies demand—and perhaps necessarily so—that man in wartime must be prepared to lay down his life for his neighbors, his family, his community and his country. But in the day-to-day business of life, it is certainly becoming increasingly clear that if man does not respect himself, like himself, and love himself, he cannot like, respect, and love his neighbors. He must first accept himself before he can be a good neighbor.

Returning to the importance of the concepts which we hold of ourselves, one may say of our earlier beliefs of ourselves that they represent a slow accumulation and a much slower discarding of working premises which men and women down the centuries have used to explain themselves and their world. These working premises were based on rule-of-thumb methods and, with the course of time, many of them became twisted away from their original setting, as, for instance, the concept that one somehow acquired virtue by dietary observance. Others were used to form building blocks for some ecclesiastical system or some traditional folkway, and hence have been perpetuated with the assistance of all the formidable self-preservatory devices with which they are equipped. One may cite here, for instance, the belief that the brave man is never afraid, or that a nice woman is never sexually aroused save when married, and then only discreetly.

Above all, almost every conception which we have had of human nature has been biased by beliefs as to how people should be, rather than being grounded upon how they actually are. For instance, there is a wide belief that mothers naturally love their children. Anyone who has the remotest acquaintance with the actualities of human nature realizes that this is far from being the universal case and that a proportion of women not only are indifferent to their children, but dislike them and wish, and sometimes say, that it would have been better had they never been born.

Our new world demands a revision of our fundamental ideas about ourselves, and the rigorous methods of inquiry afforded by the social sciences provide the means for that revision. What are we really doing, why are we doing it and where are we going?

The world that lies awaiting us is neither easy nor safe; it is most assuredly not safe unless we come to it prepared. It is a world infinitely large, promising, full of powers, beneficent or malignant as we make them. But we are creatures above all others, aggressive and resolute, and determined tremendously to expand our control over this world and all that it promises.

When the great forward movement in industry during the middle of the nineteenth century produced a series of new illnesses, we did not recoil when men and women fell sick and died in great numbers from exposure to metallic dust, such as lead. They died from exposure to other kinds of dust such as asbestos, or to industrial gases; but in the end this new industrial realm was made safe. Respirators, blowing apparatus, special ways of grinding, new kinds of material, all contributed to this end of allowing people to do what they could not previously do without danger to health and life. Still another area into which we have thrust our way is the great depths and great heights. Fifty

149

years ago it was hazardous in the extreme to work in the compressed caissons which are necessary for the building of subways and tunnels under the rivers where a great deal of water had to be kept back under high air pressure. A hundred years ago the earliest pioneers in the air lost their lives from lack of oxygen. In the first balloon ascents many a man died because he was not aware of oxygen lack. Now these things are at an end and we are able to go ten miles into the air with safety, and a mile or more into the depths of the sea. At this very hour we are engaged in forcing our way into another region where man has never hitherto been able to go with impunity, and that is into the area of atomic radiation. And already, by shielding, special clothing, and by testing every inch of the way, this too is becoming safe for us, this too is coming under our control.

So far, we have conquered these new realms by modifying them or protecting ourselves when we enter them. But this new world which lies before us is not one of radiation or of densities crushingly heavy or explosively light, nor yet of corroding chemicals. It is one of unexplored ways of living, of different forms of human relationship, of ideas for ever opening and expanding into new horizons— ideas of probability and not of certainty, of change and not of permanence. To enter it requires not material modifications, not the protection of the sealed chamber and protective clothing, but changes in our very selves. We have come to recognize—and this may be one of the great advances of our times—that the strength which we can build into our personalities, the buttressing which we can set up in our ways of life, will determine how far we can go into this new world—a world waiting for us with such vast powers, with vistas of space undreamed of by the early voyagers, with promises of control over our destiny which may forever free us from the harassments of illness, of loss and of the deadening struggle with our neighbors and within ourselves. Those who would enter and master that world must first divest themselves of ways of living, of ideas and conceptions which would render them immediately vulnerable to its tensions and stresses.

To illustrate this, I want to talk to you about certain great weaknesses in the structure of our ways of living, weaknesses which are inevitably repeated in our personalities. They form deep contradictions within us; they create hidden flaws in all of us. Some, under special stress, open up into ever-progressing maladjustments to life. Of these great weaknesses, I shall discuss three: first, our ideas of love and hate; second, the continuing struggle over the relative importance of what "is" as contrasted with what "should be"; and third, the difficulties which we run into when we try to substitute our image of a rational man for the realities of the total man.

From our very earliest days, our culture is at great pains to set up love and hate as though they were not only different, but were eternal antagonists. We learn, almost as soon as we can talk, about good fairies who love and protect you, and bad witches who hate you and will try to destroy you. Later we are introduced to a variety of gods and devils who again exemplify this eternal struggle between love and hate. At still more sophisticated levels of our lives, we learn to talk about undying and unchanging love, about parents who will always love us no matter what happens. In a broader field, we encounter men and women who say that they never fight, that they never quarrel, that they never feel angry, that it is never worthwhile. It is only when we turn from this to a careful study of the matter that doubt begins to creep in.

At the beginning of the century there was very little scientific knowledge of the relationship of love and hate, and their constant coexistence in the same individual with regard to the same person, at the same time, although some of those most penetrating of human observers, the poets of an earlier period, had frequently pointed out the ease with which great love turned to great hate. With the rapid growth of our knowledge of the personality, this concept of the relationship of love and hate has become general, first, within scientific circles. Now, it is gradually passing on, as is customary, into the field of general public knowledge, although here it is still the possession of only a few.

More recently, some of us have found it very useful to expand this concept and to go much beyond it. First, with regard to the expansion, we have come to see that all the great emotions, all those great responses which move and sweep individuals—such as love, anger and fear, sexual responsiveness and, perhaps, pain—might better be put together as a single basic response: namely, the intensification reaction. This is because all of them have much more in common than they have separating them. We have also come to realize that where the relationship between two people has for long been dominated by one or other facet of this intensification response—has, for instance, been one of hate, or of intense love, or of fear—the fact that there has been a relationship (and an intense relationship at that) is more important than the sign. In other words, it is more important, in understanding the personalities involved, to realize that there has been an intense relationship than to think in terms of a relationship of hatred or of love. One of the reasons why it is more important is that no matter whether the relationship has been one of hate or one of love, the individuals concerned become adjusted and adapted to that relationship. If one of the individuals is a child, then as he or she grows, it will be with an adaptation to the kind of relationship and, therefore, with a need for that kind of relationship. This, of course, leads to great confusion in people's minds, and great puzzlement about the behavior of such an individual, since ordinary, everyday thinking would lead one to expect that the girl brought up in fear and hatred of a tyrannical father would, when she married, certainly seek out somebody in whom the father's characteristics were not present. But this is far from being the case. For, either apparently blinding herself to the true situation, she marries someone very like this, or, strangely enough, as the marriage progresses she tends, by the expression of her unconscious needs for that kind of person, to evoke in her husband behavior which at least bears a similarity to that shown by her father.

This exceedingly interesting observation has led us to go far past the simple expansion of the older idea of the coexistence of love and hate and has brought us to another which may have even more far-reaching consequences. If it is adopted, we shall see that our ideas of love and hate consist in what might be termed a somewhat premature and superficial description of a far more basic aspect of human behavior—namely, of relationship.

Many of even the most modern contributions to this field continue to assert the individual's basic need for affection. But our studies have brought us beyond this, to the realization that affection is not enough, that still more basic than affection is the need for a relationship which is to the individual, and that relationship need not necessarily be one in which affection is predominant. Time and again we have encountered persons who have declared that they had affection showered upon them by their parents but that they were never understood—and by affection I do not mean simply material gifts but also time and devotion, care and everything which might seem to outsiders to constitute affection. Yet these persons felt they were not understood, and consequently were bitterly resentful and felt deeply deprived.

To grasp this, one should go back to a set of ideas which has never been properly developed, and that is that the individual, the human being, is incomplete in himself. Quite clearly, he has functions which cannot be fulfilled except in the presence of others. The function of reproduction is one; breast-feeding is another; and there are many other culturally determined functions—such as those which maintain our equanimity, our peace of mind through talking things out—which require the presence of others. In each of us, earlier experience determines something of the form which these functions will take, and determines, too, what will satisfy these functions, what will give us a sense of completion.

Armed with this, let us now turn back again and we shall see that what the individual must have from his fellows (his basic need from his fellows) is a satisfying relationship, and that the form which this satisfying relationship should take depends vastly on his earlier experiences. It may not be at all a relationship of love, nor one in which affection is dominant in its manifestations.

Since psychiatry is a science which must act as well as study, it is inevitable that one must go forward from this point and say: "What can we do about this continuing confusion concerning love and hate?" Here let me put forward a general solution—namely, the strengthening and fitting of ourselves to enter into our future. We must see to it that the facts which are now pouring out in ever-increasing numbers from our great social science laboratories, from our research hospitals and other investigating centers, are made available as rapidly as possible, not only so that they can be used in changing the preparation of our future citizens, our children, but also so that they can be used immediately by those of us in our adult years who have many of the crucial decisions still awaiting us.

There is a natural alliance between the home and the school and the social science research centers, an alliance which has not yet been adequately structured but which must one day be put into operation. Through such an alliance there can be passed out at once the knowledge which we have concerning the inevitable intermingling of love and hate in all our relationships; and we can go beyond this and begin to stress the extraordinary importance of relationship and the fitness of the individual for relationship. Finally, we can take the extremely important step of trying to reach a decision as to the kind of needs which we wish to see set up in our children, and can determine, at the same time, the kinds of ways in which those needs will be met.

I turn now to the second great rift in our cultural pattern, reflected as it is in the personality structure of each and all of us. This is the extremely difficult problem of the reconciliation of the "is" and the "ought." This problem is so touchy that it is quite often left severely alone. But until a good solution is found, an enormous amount of confusion, of personality impairment and of frank breakdown under stress is to be expected.

It is undoubtedly one of the most dangerous rifts in our cultural pattern. It is occasioned by the struggle for domination on the part of two ways of thinking about ourselves. On the one hand, there is a way of thinking about ourselves in terms of how things actually are; on the other hand, there is its great rival—namely, thinking about ourselves in terms of how things should be. One supposes that these two ways have been present from time immemorial. There is no doubt that at certain periods in history (and we are now emerging from such a period) one or the other of these ways of thinking about things achieves considerable dominance. It may reasonably be said that the immediate past has seen the supremacy of the way of thinking about ourselves in terms of how things should be. The great advantage of this approach is that it is possible to set up easily applied standards—sometimes too easily applied. It is possible, without having to go into a great deal of difficulty and detail, to say immediately that such and such an individual deviates in his behavior from a given standard —in a word, he is bad. We have standards for the industrious man, for the good man, for the kind man and for the generous man. It is possible, also, for society to set up a system of reward and punishment, by which what we call "good deeds" can be rewarded, and behavior of which society does not approve, suitably punished. One recognizes this procedure running all the way from the nursery school to the penitentiary.

One of the great weaknesses of this system, of course, is that its continual insistence on how things should be results in obscuring things as they are. Insistence, for instance, that women should be pure from the sexual point of view means that every woman is intent on covering up the fact that she does deviate somewhat from the standard; in consequence, we get a progressively more fictitious picture of the actual sexual behavior of women. And then, when somebody does come along, as Kinsey has, and attempts with the best possible means available to describe what is actually happening to women, there is an enormous hubbub, and a vast number of people immediately try to prove that he is wrong. No doubt, he is wrong in certain respects, but most objective-minded people are inclined to think he is more right than most people have been before him.

One great disadvantage from which this system of thinking in terms of "ought" must of necessity suffer is that its standards, buttressed as they are by very considerable emotional forces, tend to get progressively out of date. They are always behind, not only in actual practice, but they even fall behind the aspirations of the more enlightened members of the population. And finally, they offer, unfortunately, an unrivaled opportunity for power-seeking groups and organizations to control their neighbors by keeping them in a constant state of embarrassment and uneasiness, in a state of feeling anxious and guilty because the standards which are set up are nearly always completely impossible to fulfill, and everybody falls short. Hence, everybody who accepts these standards—and the vast majority do— is apt to feel chronically guilty. Furthermore, such organizations usually have ways of relieving people from feeling guilty: "Just hew to the party line and all will be well; devote yourself to the party and all will be forgiven."

One can see that the road here passes very quickly over to authoritarianism, with its insistent urge to undermine the whole democratic system. Authoritarianism does not mean to let the individual mature. Its deadly intent is to hold on to a part of the person's basis of security, by controlling his early personality formation in the home, by dominating the schools, by managing the morals, and by reaching a curbing hand into all the media of communication. Authoritarianism holds on to part of his sense of security much as it might hold on to a hostage. It will never allow the individual to be the final judge of his own conduct: that has to be decided for him by somebody else, by a "big brother."

It is obvious that this conflict between rival ways of thinking about ourselves in our day is greatly sharpened by a variety of things. The first is the great and compelling necessity for us to know the actual facts of human behavior. Nearly everyone wants to know. The mother wants to know the facts of the child-parental relations; she no longer wants to be told fairy tales about mother love—she wants to know how mothers and children really get along, how they may best get along. The industrialist wants to know all about the human factor in industry. The army wants to know what men can stand, what percentage of losses they can take, how much fatigue, how much protection they can be given by disciplining, how much risk one runs of destroying initiative.

Whether one goes to the courtroom or to the expert on traffic accidents, or whether one is planning a national sales campaign—everywhere, men and women need to have the facts concerning human nature. They want to have a statement about what "is"; and they don't want to find that they are presented with what "ought to be" as a substitute for what "is."

Another great force which is tending to swing the balance in favor of our thinking more and more in terms of what "is" rather than "ought" is the growth of the social sciences. As we all know, science is the way of thinking about things which demands answers to the questions of "how" and "why"; whereas the "ought" thinking about things demands an answer to the question of "what."

It would be idle and superficial, however, for us to say that the obvious solution is that we should eliminate all thinking in terms of "ought." In actuality, we have to see both the "is" and the "ought" kinds of thinking as aspects of human behavior. Because they are aspects of human behavior, both have to be given consideration, a place in our march to that great goal of rendering ourselves happier and more efficient.

Very briefly, we may say that "is" is a realistic way of thinking, and "ought" is the idealistic aspect of our thinking. Again, both have a place. But our idealism and our aspirations have to be based upon the realities of the situation. We cannot possibly set up as ideals things which have no hope whatsoever of being realized in terms of the facts of human behavior. Hence our first task must be a very careful survey of what is actually happening, and then a constant revision of what we would like to see happening. Thereafter, we can set up our imperatives in terms of "ought"; but they cannot be allowed to become fixed imperatives or to become a possession of some power-hungry institutions and organizations. They have to be continually revised as we gain more and more knowledge about ourselves.

Let us now look at the third of these great rifts in our social structure, from which so many difficulties in our personal lives well up. This third great rift consists in a curious oversimplification of our picture of ourselves. To put it in a few words, it consists in our assertion that we are rational individuals rather than total individuals.

As part of the great struggle to increase our control over

events, there has been, of necessity, a continuous, century-long battle with older, magical and mystical interpretations and explanations of life and of ourselves. It is a maneuver which seems inherent in mankind that when man comes to a problem which is too difficult and too complex for satisfactory solution he will attempt, at all cost, to gain some control over the situation, even if he has to resort to simplification so extreme as to exclude much of the problem with which he is struggling. This over-simplification is represented by the creation of our image of the rational man: man who is guided by logic, who reacts to a given set of circumstances in a predictable way. This conception of the logical, rational man was given immense impetus, of course, during the rapid growth of science in the eighteenth and nineteenth centuries, and by the rapid expansion of the machine—the machine in many ways becoming the prototype by means of which we tried to understand ourselves.

In the course of the process, a great deal of the total behavior of the individual had to be excluded. Where it was not excluded, it was deprecated. In consequence of this oversimplification, there arose a number of ideas which are still with us, and yet they cause us great difficulties because they are so ineffective. Among them is the will power myth—the idea that you can do anything that you want to, provided you try hard enough. The anxiety, the guilt and the endless frustration which this myth has occasioned in the patient struggling with his illness, the alcoholic with his addiction, and the sexual deviant with his impulses, is almost unbelievable.

It seems highly probable, moreover, that in the process of denying our instinctive and impulsive life, in the process of repressing what seemed nonrational, we have lost a great deal, and perhaps lost particularly in our potential creativeness. We have undoubtedly lost an enormous amount in our capacities to understand ourselves and each other. All of us are certainly acquainted with individuals who are completely imperceptive, who simply cannot understand any behavior save at the most superficial level. We know these convention-bound people who cannot think save in terms of the orthodox, but who nonetheless carry, deeply buried in repression, all that might have added and enriched lives, could it have found expression.

Still another consequence of this attempt to suppress important aspects of ourselves is that many of us repress so much that it is almost as though we had a second person within us—someone who constantly endangers the first by attempting to take over. This expresses itself in the very widespread fears that people have of losing control, of losing their minds, and, in a still more widespread form, in fears of breakdown and in fears of mental illness. There arises an aversion to mental illness, an aversion spreading out and covering the whole field of mental health, so that this great area of medicine has never had the full public support which it should have had. We dread what we have struggled so hard to control. The dread is built up by our society, which threatens us with the direst penalties if we do not control our instinctive life. These dreads run to such extremes in our society as to make Robert Louis Stevenson's story of Dr. Jekyll and Mr. Hyde one of widest and most anxiety-loaded appeal.

Actually, once we have learned to accept what we have so sedulously repressed, once we have made friends with the man within us, we find him far from threatening—and, in very fact, the completion of our nature.

I would suggest, therefore, that the personality of the

future must be one capable of tolerating in awareness a large proportion of what most of us now are able to carry only in our unconscious. This rather revolutionary idea undoubtedly would bring very extensive changes; but, with even less doubt, it would bring with it a great enrichment of life.

It is hoped that our next great adventure, that mankind's next pioneer march, will not be into some new continent—for there are none—but will be into this promising world of ourselves. Here is the place where all great things are accomplished; where all ideas take form; where all the marches, in the last analysis, are planned; where their execution is determined. Without human purpose and planning, no gun would ever be built, let alone fired; no atomic bomb would ever take form, nor be any threat to us. We are now standing on the shores of an illimitable sea, a sea dark with storms and shrouded with mystery, a sea across which none but man has strength to steer.

PSYCHOSOMATIC NOTIONS—
A REVIEW

By *Aldwyn B. Stokes, C.B.E., M.A., B.M. (Oxford)*
M.R.C.P. (London), F.R.C.P. (C.)

ALL OF US HAVE *general* notions about our minds and our bodies as an inevitable consequence of our being bound to history. Over the centuries before us men have reflected, have developed ideas about themselves, have sharpened the concepts, and have handed them on to posterity. In the processes of time these have receded into the background of "taken for granted" generalities but nonetheless are importantly there. We also have *particular* notions on mind-body relationships because of a self-awareness illuminating our living and forcing us, more or less continuously, to attend to our own nature, what we are doing, what is happening to us, and the consequences for ourselves and for others.

Further, each of us combines these general background, and particular foreground notions into a highly individual pattern of thinking. Taken together the patterns are extraordinarily diverse and variously compounded of myth, and subjective-objective experience. Thus, for example, we have all experienced occasions of fatigue and have searched in our thinking for an explanation. The explanations of

163

different people might range through a whole gamut, from moral sloth on the one hand, to the surmised effects of some chance infection on the other.

It is certain that the double-barrelled shotgun-word, "psychosomatic," will conjure up different targets even among the expert medical hunters. Some will anticipate more or less precise information on the causation of stomach ulcers, or asthma, or migraine, or the like; others will look for a penetrating analysis of those psychological complexities which issue in a bodily complaint. Some will expect scientific physiology and common sense humanity; others will hope for fluent psychodynamics and primal organ function. Few might wish to range beyond the human species, pursuing an enquiring interest in, say, "the causes of impotence in bulls" or "the nature of hysterical fits in dogs," although problems like these are an ever-present concern to veterinary surgeons, keepers of zoological gardens and the like. To wander back through time, away from the modern age might be more attractive —to rediscover, for example, the psalmist's psychosomatic plight: "I am poured out like water and all my bones are out of joint; my heart is like wax; it is melted in the midst of my bowels. My strength is dried up like a potsherd; and my tongue cleaveth to my jaws."

However, in whatever manner expert interests and expectancies may show themselves, their best summations will never achieve an absolute truth. Man seeking to understand himself may be likened to man seeking to understand his world. In 1474 Toscanelli, the geographer, inferred that the world was round and urged a westward way to attain the east; in his thought there was no inkling of a western hemisphere. Mercator, in 1569, had no doubt of a new world. His dispositions were thoroughly up to

date for his times and based on the new navigational techniques as witnessed by an ever-increasing body of intelligent, enthusiastic, capable explorers. Mercator would have
argued stoutly with the best of reasons, for the rightness of
his charts: to his posterity, namely ourselves, they are
grossly distorted—in part nonsensical. In short, to be at a
growing point of knowledge has implications for error as
well as for truth.

In terms of the historical geographic analogy the New
World of our theme, perhaps after some argument, is that
of the psychological, the Old, that of the physical. The
former is less developed scientifically, with a less precise
language: the latter is more technically equipped, more
ordered as to manifest law, more disciplined as to expression. But trafficking between the two is increasing at a
tremendous rate and, although communication is still
polyglot, it is clear that a mutual absorption of ideas,
hitherto regarded as alien, is allowing collaborative enterprise. To look at and appraise such commerce, to see the
mergence as neither a submergence nor an emergence of
one or the other party, to estimate a well-founded whole
enterprise in the future, is our present purpose.

From the foregoing, it is apparent that the approach is
from the position that:

1. All of us, commonly, conduct ourselves on the basis
of personal strongholds of opinion on mind-body relationships.

2. Our sense of healthy individuality tends to preclude
relating our notions to the determinants of time (particularly as we think of ourselves as at the peak of history) and
of species (particularly as we think of ourselves as su-
premely human).

3. Experts, on whom we rely to resolve the uneasy diffi-

Aldwyn B. Stokes

culties of our personal positions, are themselves constrained by their predilections in terms of method of thought and language.

4. Nonetheless, some kind of new whole is emerging.

A primitive attempt at depicting some glimpsed attributes of the new whole is introduced by a chart of still greater crudity than the maps of the early cartographers (Fig. 1). It is a personal effort at depicting those known interrelationships which make up a single human being, engaged in the business of living and perhaps becoming disabled in the process. The diagram represents a psychobiological organization with four elements contributing to the whole, namely, (a) the genetic field, (b) the organ or

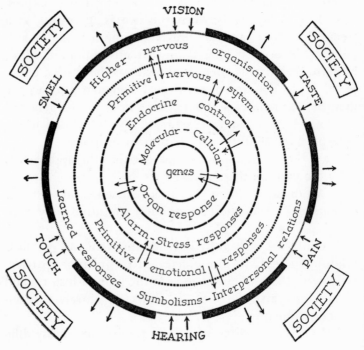

physical field, (c) the personality field, and (d) the social field.

The *genes* are represented as a germinal center making up endowment reserves which are certainly not unlimited, but which are usually sufficient for some useful activity on the life scene. They usually represent a general pattern of mobilized assets and accumulated deficits by the exercise of small individual effects, rarely by outstanding force. The genes exert their effects on molecular structure and thence on cell and organ function. A state of organ relationship comes into being with the opportunities of organ response as an aspect of reactivity. Organ function itself is related but subservient to the control of the endocrine system, particularly that of the pituitary and adrenal glands. Through the endocrines, more speedy alarm responses are initiated by chemical means, for example, the *physical* preparations for fight or flight. A slower response to stress of any kind, such as infection or trauma, is mediated by the endocrine glands and represents the field of operation of ACTH or Cortisone, now as familiar by name as insulin.

But this system is itself dominated by the central nervous system, at first primitive in its organization and concerned with crude emotional responses such as rage or fear or well-fed contentment. This primitive nervous system is itself subject to the modifying influence of a later developed nervous system. Here the personal organization is of the greatest complexity and the greatest versatility. By the complicated processes of learning, past experiences have been incorporated into the individual so that, at any time, some representation of all his past is laid down in him, as it were, in ways of feeling about his experiences, of thinking about them, and of doing something in respect to them. Symbolisms and the diversity of responses in the face of other people or things have their origin in this section of the whole to a degree which gives a unique quality to the unit—the quality of a *personality*.

However, the unique quality of the person must not be overemphasized. Individuals are as much alike as they are unlike, and their likenesses, particularly in the appreciation of hurt or joy, aid communication to one another so that coherence into groups is fostered with the formation of *societies*.

Nonetheless, the individual in his society has a strong realization of his so-called "ego" boundaries. These are strongly marked in Figure 1 with windows for the senses. In adult life vision and hearing have priority, but it must not be forgotten that in the early stages of living, taste and smell, touch and pain have been particularly important.

This chart allows a number of pertinent comments:

1. Although the chart has been built up on various layers, in terms of responsiveness, there are no impregnable barriers between the layers. Events in society can produce penetrative effects right through to the gene. Vice versa, events anywhere in the individual system achieve emergence in society. The whole is in a state of reverberation, either resonant or dissonant, to any change anywhere.

2. Events in the various parts, although perhaps concurrent and associated, are described very differently. The different descriptions arise from differing conceptual analyses and points of orientation.

3. The expanding system or organization introduces new elements at each stage, considered in terms of both quality and quantity. This is no doubt a partial explanation of the differing schemes of approach and the differing technical aids developed in the approach.

4. In at least two areas, unknowns of the greatest mag-

nitude appear without which the whole is meaningless—
namely, memory and feeling function.

The binding of memory and feeling functions in a
physically elaborated system is a crucial issue for psychosomatic theory. If the fact is not accepted, or if the fact
is accepted only as a common-sense human insight, or
accepted more specifically but with resistance to its implications, then those interactions between man and his world
which have their issue in disablement cannot be a proper
object of medical study.

The difficulty has been that our own mental experiencing is not open to observation through any sense organ.
Although it is based on factual observation of non-sensual
kind, and can be communicated so that our private observations achieve a common public acceptance, nonetheless,
until very recently, there have been no very definite ways
of relating mental events to brain events.

Today the general position is beyond dispute. As to
memory, advances in the techniques of electroneurophysi-
ology and neurosurgery have begun to tap the secrets of
the temporal lobe (e.g., Penfield and Rasmussen). Under
suitable conditions the stimulation of precisely defined
areas on the surface of the brain is associated with the
revival of past personal memories. Furthermore, the stimulation, on repetition, is attended by the same repeated
testimony. There is literally a physical incorporation of
life experience with the implication of effective relationships to all other corporeal events, including organ function. Already physiologists (e.g., Adrian) are engaged in
exploring the mechanisms of sensory incorporation and the
mediating pathways within the brain. That the problems
are complicated and will still be extant at the end of this

century should not obscure the establishment of the principle.

Three points may be noted in passing:

1. The modern experimental objective findings do not conflict with but confirm the type of introspective analysis that psychologists have long utilized to explain memory.

2. The experiences, recalled in memory, were laid down at particular times in the longitudinal axis of life development.

3. The recall has emotional connotations.

As to *feeling*, the earlier work on "fight or flight" physiology and sham rage quickly led to the discovery that the expression of emotion, in terms both of readying the body and striking an attitude, is more or less decided by the pattern of nerve outflow from the brain, particularly that part of the brain known as the hypothalamus. But emotional self-awareness, whatever its expression, is something which is part and parcel of consciousness. It is here that backtracking of neurological and neuroanatomical thinking on the early primitive parts of the brain becomes important. There are a number of notable exponents (e.g., Papez, Maclean, Cobb, LeGros, Clark) of a structural and functional reorientation which divorces most of man's primitive brain from the simpler processes of smell and remarries it to a wider involvement in those cerebral and visceral activities associated with a fluctuant response to the life scene. It is through such studies as these that the notion of a cerebral feeling tone mechanism is beginning to take objective form. Already, in a crude kind of way, a wavering measure of control can be applied in some instances of tempestuous excess of feeling (with its behavioral consequences) by operative procedures on the brain (Miller).

Here memory and feeling are emerging in the epistemo-
logical scheme of things as complicated functions served
by structures which allow the reverberations of life experience, past and present, throughout the whole body. These
happenings are the object of man's own introspection and
he gives testimony to them in terms such as pain or pleasure, he may do something about them by avoidance, or
mastery, or welcoming. But whatever he feels or whatever
he does is determined by his personal involvement in his
life scene.

Involvement has a beginning and a burgeoning. At
birth the child manifestly responds by feeling although
nothing of intellectual capacity has been mobilized. What
contribution circumstances within the womb have made
toward a pattern of feeling can only be guessed. But there
is some reason to suppose that distress, for example in
terms of deficient oxygen supply, is already playing its part
in molding the constitutional pattern. After birth, however, the mother-child separateness, with varying periods
of nursing time and variable qualities of nursing relationship, probably proscribes importantly the developing pattern of reactivity. The particular kind of mother-child
relationship is, of course, only one stimulus which pounds
into a slowly and variously developing ego system.

Little enough is known of the varying rates of structural
physiological and metabolic maturation, much less how
these rates are modified by differing patterns of stimulation
from the environs. It seems clear, however, that feeling
relationships are being laid down in the preverbal era of
infancy not only on the basis of instinctual sets and condi-
tioning but also on wordless imagery. In the years of speech
maturation a spurt and facilitation are accorded these feeling relationships around the mother and father as primary

identification figures, but with the modifying influences of kindred contacts. The mother is already beginning to be known, in the sense of being fully experienced, as warm-hearted or cold, as protective or permissive or hostile and intolerant. The father, perhaps more aloofly, assumes similar meaning. The brothers and sisters emerge in varying "for or against" patterns. In the interpersonal family scene, being a boy or girl becomes vaguely and then more surely complicated in terms of notions about the self and about others.

In short, physical and emotional-intellectual maturation are proceeding in interplay over the dimension of time. All elements in the total maturation process have a variable fostering and responsiveness to the vagaries of the environment which always have some stressful forces included in them. Always there is a flux of adjustment until the individual forces for maturation have been realized. At that time the adjustment mechanisms themselves, although many, are more or less numbered and represent the assets and deficits of the individual in material and personal living. As Grinker puts it, "Any hypothesis concerned with psychosomatic functions or pathology should deal with the intermediate stage of development between the undifferentiated whole functional pattern and the integrated matured process. It is this period that determines the formation of a healthy, sick, or potentially sick organism."

Increased knowledge of the processes of human development will certainly throw more light on the ways in which "hurt feeling" comes into being and the consequences. Painful affect might be thought of as an integrative continuum extending from pain (of direct noxious contact origin) through fear (reaction of immediate danger) to anxiety of apprehension, anxiety of conflict, and finally moral fear or guilt. A raw construct of this sort will serve to point up a relationship between feeling as a subjective experience related responsively not only to real events in their present entirety, but also to cues, more or less meaningless in their present existence, but fulminantly meaningful in terms of a symbolic organization of the past. The personal development of such an organization over the young straining years of contact with a particular social scene, forcefully represented by central nurturing and authoritative figures, is bound to be associated with dilemma, compromise, subjugations and exacerbations of feeling or, if you will, perplexity, ambivalence, inhibition or excitement. Whether the outcome, in terms of general overt behavior or acceptable-nonacceptable behavior, is more or less usual or neurotic or psychotic, there are always more *specific* bodily reverberations. The problem of the focus of these bodily reverberations immediately arises because it is the focusing which displays to the individual himself and to people around him that "something" is wrong. The "something" then becomes a "thing" with movement toward the construction of a psychosomatic disease entity.

The attempts at accounting for the particular psychosomatic symptom are, to my mind, not very satisfactory, taken separately.

1. *The Psychological*—That the emergence in the life pattern of a focused physical effect (regarded as pathological, disabling, or "not as it should be") represents a direct end result of an initiating psychological process involving a personal symbolic organization, is not only far-fetched but conflicts with the biological principle of change-exchange relationships in communicating systems. How far

the organ or part, about to become the focus of disturbance in the physical sense, can indicate its preselection in the symbolic organization of the individual has not been a matter of investigation as far as I know.

2. *The Physical*—The idea of local defect which becomes involved in local stresses occasioned by the physiological pulsations of the long-maintained emotional disturbance can be given a proper weight where the local defect is amply demonstrated. Even then, however, the causes of the defect itself cannot be relegated conveniently and nihilistically to constitution, at any rate, without taking care to look at the defect as the possible irreversible result of interplays that previously had been reversible.

3. *"Fight" or "Flight" Physiology of Emotion*—The "whole" responses to the life scene have patterns of feeling (subjective) and physical effect (objective) which together have recognizable components, some major and dominant, some minor and subjugated. That the physical places of "excess" or "famine" effect might become vulnerable when the whole response is perpetuated or facilitated is understandable. But human physiological studies have not yet been sufficiently penetrating to extend much beyond the older concepts of "fight or flight" physiology.

4. *Focused Physiology of Emotion*—The tendency to pick out one organ or one effect in a situation of relatively gross responsiveness, although frequently a necessity imposed by limitations of time and place, opportunity and technical instrumentation, probably does scant justice to the bodily reverberations of which each human body is emotionally capable. The physiology of "appeal" in rela-

tionship to asthma is a growing point of this sort but other possibilities might come to mind.

5. *Physiological Regression*—Any physiology of adult emotion must take into account physical maturation and the earlier life stages of responsiveness on which the adult responsiveness is built up. The notion of a physiological regression to an earlier life stage of operation is an intriguing one, although there are relatively few facts available at the moment to allow any definite explanations of the specific psychosomatic symptom in terms of a vegetative retreat.

Although it has been said that not one of these current constructs is sufficient in itself to provide a satisfactory explanation of the focusing of a psychosomatic disability, nonetheless, taken together, all or in part, they provide a useful framework of approach to the patient suffering the disability and requiring help in its regard. Practical problems of where to direct major effort in line with psychological and physiological plasticity of response and modifiability are expediently answered by recourse to that framework.

Plasticity of response arises particularly in the psychosomatic disorders of the young where, in terms of the personally developing symbol organization of themselves and their world, the symptom is more directly manipulated for gainful purpose. Functions of eating, urinating, defecating, breath holding and the like are frequently used at near conscious level as a means of controlling or modifying parental relationships or asserting kinship position. This kind of assertive maneuvering extends sometimes to the material elements of the child-parent relationship so that,

175

for example, the dietary procedures and syringe techniques of the diabetic child become linked with two-way coercions. There may be drastic consequences reflected back on the child by the changed attitude of the mother, and the child's awareness of the change will in its turn begin a process which may issue in overt adult neuroticism. Here the childhood psychosomatic problems seem more aggressive or more passive according to whether their basic purpose is hostility or the securing of yet more love. It would be useful work to follow the two categories through into adult life beyond the phase of "growing out" of the symptomatic disturbance.

The notion of "growing out" of a symptomatic disturbance has little enough meaning, but such as it has is related to inclusion within enlarging groups of people, particularly peer groups of school fellows and the like. Within the cultural pattern of the peer groups and through their exchanges the symptom can be stamped in or released. Free discussion of problems of interpersonal relationships within the school classes is being encouraged by progressive educators. For example, a very careful study in one school system under conditions of strict control showed a marked alleviation of somatic plaintiveness in a group of high school pupils who for a six-month period had engaged regularly in free discussion groups. Both the problem and the method of attack remind us of similar instances (e.g., among soldiers complaining of "effort syndrome") and of the slowly developing group work in various fields of psychosomatic medicine (e.g., stuttering, dyspepsias and the like).

The importance of maturation processes and group effects is beyond doubt when consideration is given to the social aspects of psychosomatic medicine. A number of distinguished anthropologists and social psychologists have given repeated emphasis to the developmental aspects of cultural incorporation, that culture is not outside but within each of us. Their dynamic concepts of change-exchange relationships offer an explanation of the differing psychosomatic symptoms and mechanisms in different racial, national, vocational, religious, and possibly other groups. They help us to remember also that the dimension of time is operative and that fashions of psychosomatic expression may be as epochal as other modes of expression.

Halliday has pointed up the time theme by reporting the shift in morbidity rates between 1900 and 1930 in perforating peptic ulcer, hypertension and other psychosomatic disorders. The shifts include change of sex incidence and age vulnerability. Similarly in this social field of investigation, Ryle has noted the differential spread of functional illness across different social classes. That physicians of this sort are concerning themselves more and more with the community relationships of medical science and practice is an indication of a renewed awareness of the focal point of the doctor in the field of public mental health.

Most practicing physicians, probably intuitively by establishing rapport with their patients, make rough judgments on the social and personality factors interwoven with the physical in their ill patients. Despite a modern redefinition of the objectives of undergraduate medical instruction and a much greater emphasis on psychiatric principles, it is still true that precision and the confidences of precise work rest more on the side of the physical. It would seem important to press forward efforts in the constructing of more efficient instruments of personality appraisal—e.g., in psychosomatic work, the notion of emotional immaturity requires a good deal of clarification both in qualitative and quantitative terms. With such instruments available there is a likelihood that a specific personality structure will not be so readily associated with each psychosomatic disease.

In contrast to the hoped-for, and well-in-the-future, general instruments of psychosomatic survey, we must rely now on more or less elaborate experiments on bodily reactions to specific personal stresses aroused in laboratory interview situations. These experiments have the disadvantages of complicated technical organization and single choice of bodily focus, but they richly demonstrate the linkages of life situations, emotional reactions and physiological involvement.

It is more difficult, even with elaborated technical equipment and facilities, to appraise endocrine interaction in situations of life stress. Selye's work on the general adaptation syndrome has given a tremendous impetus to the study of what are probably general biological defense mechanisms. How, in human beings, those nervous discharges associated with emotional reaction to a life scene, funneled through the hypothalamus of the brain, are implicated in a general adaptation remains to be shown; what other pathways from the brain may exist more specifically for the complications of human adaptation is an unknown.

Particularly at the endocrine level of integration, however, it becomes clear that the notion of a psychosomatic process as one-way travel from psyche to soma is untenable, although useful in our present state of knowledge. Not only are excursions from soma to psyche evident but a mesh of change and exchange relationships is exposed. This is well illustrated by long-term researches in periodic catatonia where changes in psychic state, vegetative function, thyroid activity, steroid metabolism, protein formation and breakdown, blood capillary physiology, electroencephalographic changes, acne eruptions and gastric unease are all inextricably involved in orderly fashion. The teasing out of such relationships as these is the future task of psychosomatic medicine.

Lastly it must be noted that while almost all workers are alive to the genetic and constitutional factors inherent in the problems of psychosomatic disability, little work, if any, is being done with the study of twins. Here one would think is a rich material, with controls provided by nature, awaiting the researcher into the physiodynamics and psychodynamics of psychosomatic integration.

In conclusion, I revert to the historical-geographical analogy of the beginning. Man seeking to know himself has found two great continents of knowledge. Among others, the physician has had to adjust himself to the expanding scheme of things. In doing so he has formed and is continuing to form valuable alliances with other younger disciplines. Nonetheless, the adjustments will be difficult. The hope underlying this paper and the many personal opinions it presents is that the outcome will be felicitous for an ultimate new "whole" of medicine.

MAN AND HIS NUTRITION

By Charles Glen King, Ph.D., D.Sc.

DURING THE PAST few years I have had an opportunity to study nutrition practices in Central America, for the purpose of developing long-range plans by
which the United Nations and other agencies might work
to best advantage on behalf of the public. The United
Nations agencies are especially concerned about the rural,
village and low-income groups, where modern management has not reached the stage of raising standards of
living. The experiences of first-hand observations are un-
forgettable. Yet I could not escape frequent surprises at
finding how clearly research and technical progress here in
the United States and Canada has made a rich contribution
toward solving their problems, and conversely, how often
their progress is of value here. Medical research can be
conducted there to the advantage of everyone, and we as
well as they gain by their advances in health, education
and productive capacity.

Conditions in the Central American countries serve to
illustrate the critical nature of food problems in many
other areas. Encouraging progress is under way to improve
agricultural, medical and educational practices in Central
America, but a large proportion of the population—perhaps 80 per cent—still consumes a diet that consists largely
of corn and beans. This diet pattern is followed by the
native Indians and by a large fraction of the Ladino

("Western Culture") portion of the population. Adults and children eat significant amounts of fresh fruits, but the consumption of animal protein foods, such as meat, milk, fish and eggs, and green leafy vegetables, is extremely low.

Children from weaning time to four or five years of age fare much worse than older groups. They go directly from weaning onto a diet that consists almost solely of corn "pancakes" (tortillas) and boiled beans. The corn is prepared by soaking in lime water, grinding to a paste of fine meal, and cooking on a flat iron surface or a hot stone. A pickup of calcium during the lime-water treatment represents an important gain, but the protein content of this diet simply will not permit normal human growth or health.

Enough fresh fruit grows everywhere and is consumed in sufficient quantities by adults and small children to prevent widespread scurvy, but good quality protein, vitamin A, and iodine intakes tend to be extremely low. The intakes of iron, fluorine, riboflavin and vitamin B_{12} are often also low; but there is very little information about many of the other trace mineral elements and vitamins.

The net effect among children in the one- to five-year age range is to induce a state of malnutrition that is severe enough to arrest skeletal development and growth in height or weight. Until about one year of age, the course of skeletal, height and weight development is about equal to that found in children here. Beyond five years of age, growth is resumed gradually among those who survive, until it reaches almost a normal rate per year. Finally, growth tapers off shortly after adolescence without regaining the net loss incurred before age five. The net effects on physical stature are fairly clear, representing a stunting equivalent of about two to three years' growth, but no one can yet estimate satisfactorily the damage that is done to the later functional health of the body internally.

Death rates from malnutrition among the small children are very high—reaching to one third to one half of the total population under the age of five in some areas, although the official records are grossly inadequate and misleading. Since the terminal stages are generally characterized by diarrhea and other physical signs of illness, the records of the cause of death (commonly reported by the family or neighbors) are far from accurate. Physicians generally do not sign death certificates.

Frank cases of the deficiency disease caused by a low intake of good quality protein foods are called *kwashiorkor,* or in Spanish, *sindrome pluricarencial infantil.* These cases are found regularly on most of the pediatric wards of the hospitals and frequently among informal groups of children observed with their mothers at work in fields or at home. The condition of a child with typical *kwashiorkor* is generally characterized by cessation of growth, edema or swelling, darkened and patchy skin, hair that is "dry" and reddish in color instead of a normal black, diarrhea, distinct mental apathy and a tendency to whimper. Fatty, enlarged livers and distended abdomens are generally evident during early stages of the disease. The pancreas also shows a failure to secrete the necessary digestive enzymes. Unless the changes have progressed too far, convalescence follows the feeding of such foods as milk, meat, eggs or fish to furnish a generous supply of good quality protein, vitamins and minerals.

The physicians who have studied the injury to glandular tissue in children coming to autopsy are convinced that many of those who survive never reach normal levels of health. To a degree, the injuries may be reversible, but the liver, pancreas and intestinal wall, for example, are often damaged permanently without causing death. Injury to the nervous system can scarcely be appraised. This area of medical research will be watched with great interest, I believe, because of the information furnished for the study of chronic diseases in areas like our own, where breaks in health may not be evident in earlier years, but occur increasingly in adult life.

The conditions which are described with specific reference to Central America are not greatly different from those that can be found among populations that characterize a large part of the tropical and subtropical sections of the world, wherever technological development has failed to reach areas having a high population density and inadequate education. The general pattern of diets in such areas is characterized by a high intake of corn, rice, millet or starchy root crops, supplemented by peas and beans, but characterized by poor quality proteins.

One is impressed with the contribution that scientific advances in other countries can make toward the solution of problems in agriculture and medicine where nutritional conditions are extremely poor. For example, the work of Dr. William C. Rose at the University of Illinois has established the human requirement for protein fragments necessary to protect human health—the so-called essential amino acids. Hence the chemist, agriculturalist, and physician can appraise the food resources in every community in terms of this basic protein requirement. The information not only guides the immediate practical plans for producing and distributing foods of superior quality, but it also guides the geneticist in his attempt to develop new plant and animal foods having an optimum balance of amino acids. The meat processor in Chicago draws upon the same basic information as the corn hybridizer in Guatemala or Iowa, who wants to improve the food supply.

Again, new methods for measuring the specific content of vitamins, minerals, and proteins in extremely minute quantities of material, such as a few drops of blood, make it possible for teams of physicians and biochemists to identify the specific nature of deficiencies in an area where corrective measures are being planned. The same techniques are equally useful in appraising the nutritional status of population groups in areas where health is at the mere survival level, or in New York City, where levels of nutrition are relatively high. In Central America, for example, the content of vitamin A, vitamin B_2, and vitamin C in the blood serum has made it possible to identify the relative need for these nutrients in each individual area under investigation. It was also possible to identify the low content of specific digestive enzymes circulating in the blood and thus to demonstrate the atrophy of the glandular tissue which leads to extremely poor utilization of food. These tests offer promise of detecting deficiencies in advance of a critical break in health.

It may be asked, very naturally, what can be done when large sections of the country are faced with such appalling agricultural and nutritional problems as one finds in India, Central America or Africa. The worst policy, I believe, is to adopt a defeatist attitude and act as if the situation were hopeless. In contrast, one can identify specific and broad lines of progress that offer promise for great improvements within a reasonable length of time. For example, in the Central American countries, an extension of the powdered milk distribution program supported by the United Nations and by the local governments can be used to accomplish two goals at the same time.

First, there is a direct human service and a demonstration of improvements in the health of large groups of children in each of the countries. These demonstrations can be developed as educational channels to radiate out through the adjacent villages, rural areas, and cities, to reach the greater part of the population.

Also, improved child health makes an appeal to people in every stratum of society. Good evidence on that basis can win economic and political support for the requisite health and agricultural improvements. When there is a reasonable degree of cooperation between the local ministries of health, agriculture, education, and economic development, local industries and farm organizations can cooperate in the development of long-range plans by which substantial progress can be made at a rate that is really gratifying. Strategically placed dairy farms and processing plants are proving to be successful ventures. They are on a sound economic basis that can be relied upon to make a major contribution toward further developments.

A successful dairy industry goes a long way toward stimulating interest among farmers in the use of adequate fertilizers, in the construction of silos and granaries, in feeding to maintain high milk production throughout the year, in the importance of sanitation, and in education of adults and children in the principles of good nutrition.

Two other advantages from a dairy industry can be seen in the stimulus to increased production and consumption of green, leafy foods and grains that are essential both for improved production of livestock and for better direct foods for human consumption.

In areas adjacent to the seacoast there is a prospect of improving health and the national economy by increasing the production of fishery products. These developments are still on a relatively small scale.

In the long run, outside help can be most efficient when

used in support of research and demonstration projects in which a training program is included to develop leadership and economic resources within each country. Economic aid then has a reasonable prospect of reaching its objectives.

We should not lose sight of the fact that in most of the countries where conditions looked very discouraging twenty years ago, rapid progress is now being made. Much of the so-called climatic handicap to agriculture and human health has been proved to be, instead, a failure to understand the importance of crop selection, modern fertilizer practice for good plant yields, and the nutritional requirements of man and his animals.

Turning now to our own specific problems in the United States, we have long since passed the stage where there is an appreciable risk of starvation in terms of energy requirements, or calories. There is a generous supply of high-quality foods that contain enough nutrients to furnish us with an ideal diet for everyone. Then why do we not have roughly optimum nutrition for everyone?

The best starting point to answer this question, I believe, is to point out some of the specific advances that have been made only recently. But when we look into the future there is a tendency to be uncertain of the further progress that can be made.

We have an enormous advantage in that industry has become alert to take advantage of scientific and educational advances, and we have good cooperation between industry and government agencies in working toward higher levels of health and increased service to the public.

We have long been in a favored position among the nations with respect to having adequate sources of good quality animal protein foods. We are in a leading position with respect to the sanitary and nutritional quality of other foods as well. Broadly speaking, the production and processing of our food supply have kept the cost within a range that permits all strata of society to purchase the requisite quantities of all known nutrients. However, education and a willingness to purchase foods on a nutritional basis still present serious problems.

We have had a constantly rising efficiency in the production of nearly all the major foodstuffs, including dairy products, grain, beef, pork, poultry, fish, citrus fruit, green leafy and yellow vegetables, potatoes, tomatoes and small fruit—temporarily beyond our management capacity for consumption and marketing. These advances, accompanied by technical improvements in the products consumed, have carried us from a period when scurvy due to vitamin C deficiency, rickets due to vitamin D deficiency, pellagra due to protein and niacin deficiency, and goiter due to iodine deficiency were widespread—estimated to have affected from one half to two thirds of our total population—to our present freedom from these diseases, in a practical sense. Enrichment of bread and other cereals has gone a long way toward improving our national intake of four nutrients: vitamin B_1, niacin, riboflavin, and iron. The addition of vitamin A to margarine also represents a distinct gain. Vitamin D milk and iodized salt represent two more notable gains. These advances have come almost entirely within the past twenty-five years. A new major advance in building good health by adequate nutrition is just getting under way in about 1,100 American cities by fluoridation of water supplies. This measure lowers the prevailing high incidence of tooth decay to somewhere near half its present disgracefully high level.

There is every reason to feel confident that continuing gains of this kind will be made in proportion to our support of research and education. Among the current intensive demands for improvements in health that appear to have a relationship to nutrition, I would cite the fact that even with fluoridation of water supplies, there is still a prospect of lowering the incidence of tooth decay to a much greater degree when diets are uniformly maintained at high levels of protein, mineral and vitamin intake.

Our nutrition difficulties are in striking contrast to the situation in tropical areas, in terms of the age groups that cause the greatest worry. In the tropical areas, the most crucial group is evidently the child population in the years immediately following weaning, whereas we think of our problem as being most urgent among those in the upper age bracket, from forty to eighty. The infant (under one year) death rate in Central America, for example, is roughly three to four times the rate in the United States or Canada, and in the one to four age group, the rate is reported to be about thirty times higher than in the United States.

In contrast to the dominance of infectious diseases as a cause of death in technologically retarded countries, here, heart disease is highest as a cause of death, followed by cancer, hardening of the arteries and related vascular changes, deaths in early infancy (with accidents in first place), and then in fifth place, deaths from the combined pneumonias and influenzas (this group represents the first that is caused primarily by infections). There follows, in sequence, a high incidence of death from chronic diseases of the liver, diabetes, and kidney failure.

This recent emphasis upon degenerative diseases focuses attention upon the need for understanding how the body develops and functions. When we remain in ignorance of how the individual cells function and how different glandular tissues of the body must be kept in balance for the production of health, the medical sciences remain without the information they need to develop preventive medicine, which is the major goal of the medical profession and other leaders in public health.

One does not want to understate or overstate the case for nutrition in an approach to these degenerative diseases, but there is unquestionably a growing agreement among leaders in the medical sciences and in nutrition that a normal state of health cannot be maintained without provision for a balanced nutrient intake. This factor of balance, in addition to meeting minimum requirements, is more critical than was recognized until the last few years. A few examples will serve to illustrate the point.

An imbalance in the amino acid intake, independently of meeting minimum requirements, can rapidly induce important fatty and related degenerative changes in the liver. Furthermore, the balance among amino acids is closely associated with the intake of a number of vitamins, and vice versa. Again, excessive calorie intake tends to increase the damages caused by nutrient deficiencies and imbalances. But the reasons are not clear to account for the association of excess caloric intake (body weight) with an increased incident of diabetes, heart disease, liver failure, cancer, hardening of the arteries, and, in brief, a shortened life span. Basic research on fat synthesis and reconstruction within the body should accelerate progress in lessening the penalties imposed by these chronic diseases that are now dominant.

A related area where research interest is most intensive refers to the injuries to the blood vessels characterized by deposits of cholesterol, and the cumulative effects of different ranges of cholesterol intake, compared with disturbances in cholesterol formation and disposal. On the whole, the trend of current opinion is in the direction of attributing excessive cholesterol concentrations in the blood stream to excessive caloric intake. When the total caloric intake is markedly in excess, however, there is reason to believe that a high percentage of fat may involve more risk than low or moderate intakes. On the other hand, if the caloric intake is not too high, and if the diet as a whole is well balanced, there is no reason to believe that a moderate intake of fat is injurious. In fact, some fat to furnish the unsaturated fatty acids and a moderate source of energy is advantageous. I should like to emphasize this point because there is a tendency to misunderstand the nature of the evidence available, in so far as the public is concerned.

The work of Best and his associates at the University of Toronto has been especially striking in showing the importance of good diets in young animals, as a means of preventing or delaying the onset of degenerative diseases in middle life. Young growing animals made deficient only in choline for a short period, and then restored to a complete diet showed a high incidence of degenerative changes in the arteries, heart, liver, and other organs by the time they had reached a stage when they should have been normal adult animals. In this case, too, a high intake of calories increased the severity of the injury. Even vitamin C, which we tend to associate too simply with protection from scurvy, has been shown to have a distinct effect upon the regulation of fat and protein metabolism in the liver and other glandular tissues.

In the field of mineral metabolism, the rate of research progress is more rapid than is generally recognized. Iodine, for example, which was long associated almost solely with the hormone thyroxine, is now known to be associated with a second and similar hormone with even greater activity. Magnesium balances have scarcely been studied in relation to human health, but in the field of animal nutrition, the importance of magnesium in relation to normal bone development and the risks of excessive deposits of calcium in the muscles, heart, and blood vessels has become very clear. These experiments range all the way from guinea pigs and cotton rats to farm livestock, but the evidence in human experience is very inadequate.

The importance of salt intake as a factor of importance in heart disease and high blood pressure has long been recognized in a general way. Some salt is necessary for health, but where the optimum intake lies, on a life span basis, is not clear. Meanwhile, the problem of maintaining low sodium diets that are adequate nutritionally in other respects and attractive to one's appetite represents an area where the difficulties are still great. It is encouraging that the Toronto group has recently picked up a new lead in regard to the hormone control of salt balances and the interplay of the specialized kidney cells with changes in blood pressure and the functions of the adrenal glands. Extension of the work is under way at Washington University Medical School.

Molybdenum, cobalt, vanadium, zinc, copper, and manganese are among the more recent mineral elements to be discovered as important in plant and animal physiology. Students of cellular chemistry are now aware of the fact that these elements are among the most important catalysts in regulating cellular functions that are characteristic of practically all forms of life. In time these basic discoveries will have increasing usefulness in protecting public health.

Cobalt has its key role well identified as a constituent of vitamin B_{12} to protect against pernicious anemia. The others are still in the stage of exploration in human health, but meanwhile are proving to be useful in agriculture. More than a million acres of farm land in eastern Washington, for example, showed increased crop yields when zinc was added to the soil. The first stage is usually to achieve more efficient production of crops from soils that are naturally deficient or in a bad state of balance. The second stage is nearly always to accomplish more satisfactory growth in livestock. But always, in the past, and therefore we believe it would be true in the future, the early steps with plants and animals have been followed by advances in medical practice, either at the level of understanding how the human body functions, or suddenly, as in the case of iodine, fluorine, and cobalt, through large-scale advances sweeping the world in the improvement of human nutrition. These applications often are possible at relatively little cost to the public but with tremendous economic and health advantages.

In conclusion, one does not have to be an optimist to see in the continued advances in nutrition science, a lively prospect for continued gains in human health, in more efficient agriculture and in the broad approaches to higher standards of living. When guided by these sound principles, industry and the processes of education can be relied upon to serve the public with increasing efficiency and greater enjoyment of living.